The First
INVENTIONS
PREHISTORY TO 1200BC

Published by The Reader's Digest Association Limited
London • New York • Sydney • Montreal

Contents

Introduction

It is hard to imagine how the world would be without the inventions and discoveries of the previous generations of humankind. Just try, for a moment, to think what life would be like without writing and books, medicine, the telephone, or such common-place items as sewing needles (invented *c*16,000 BC), money (*c*700 BC) or spectacles (13th century AD). Every century or era has produced its own crop of inventions, slowly shaping the world we know today. Take, for instance, the simple technology of a wheel mounted on a chassis: first thought of in about 3500 BC, over time it gave rise (among many other things) to the chariot, the carriage, the hansom cab and the bicycle.

The Adventure of Discovery and Invention is a chronologically arranged series that tells the stories of inventions, great and small, that have transformed human lives. It reveals how technologies emerged and have evolved through the ages – sometimes through the genius of individuals, sometimes because changing conditions make the time ripe for innovation. And it shows how profoundly human ingenuity has changed society and the world around us. The stories are rich in information and anecdote: intriguing links showing how one invention leads to another; the sad tales of geniuses ahead of their time and shunned by peers; the amusing spectacle of inventors squabbling over who discovered what and when. Above all, the series offers fascinating insights into the building blocks of our modern world.

The First Inventions goes back beyond the beginnings of human history to start with the very earliest discoveries of the Stone Age – how to make stone tools and control fire. It then takes the story up to the ancient world, through the innovations of the first farmers and settlers, the Egyptians, Mesopotamians and other ancient civilisations. Perhaps most surprising is how many of their tools and inventions are still with us today.

The editors

Monuments to past ingenuity
The most celebrated legacy of ancient Egypt are the Great Pyramids of Giza, just outside Cairo. They are the only one of the Seven Wonders of the Ancient World to survive into modern times. The step pyramid at Saqqara, built a century earlier, was the first example of monumental stone architecture anywhere in the world. But the long-lasting Egyptian civilisation bequeathed much more than pyramids to the modern era.

▶ A multipurpose bifacial stone tool, shaped by a human ancestor as far back as 2 million years ago. It was used for cutting, skinning, scraping and sharpening.

▲ A Stone Age toolmaker detaches blades from a core of flint with skilful blows from a hammerstone. While the expert toolmaker works, others watch and learn.

▲ A stone lamp, made from red granite around 20,000 years ago and found at the prehistoric site of Eyziès in France.

F ar back in prehistory, millions of years ago, distant human ancestors known today as australopithecines made their homes in caves, which offered them a measure of security and refuge from the threat of danger. Generally, they would

◄ Flaming torches were used to light caverns at least 500,000 years ago.

▼ Barbed harpoons were designed for hunting big game fish. These examples were carved from reindeer antlers in the Upper Palaeolithic era.

▲ These eyed needles were carved from deer bones some 18,000 years ago.

▲ A hunter – or perhaps a warrior – with bow and arrows was painted on a rock at Tassili n'Ajjer, Algeria, c12,000 years ago.

have ventured only short distances to forage for food, such as fruits, edible roots and meat scavenged from dead animals. The wider world would have seemed an intensely hostile place – the realm of wild beasts and natural forces

► A stave carved from a reindeer antler, *c*12,000 BC.

▲ A clay model of grain storehouses in ancient Egypt, *c*2000 BC.

▲ In the Upper Palaeolithic, the invention of the spearthrower increased the power and range of a hunter's throw, enabling him to target and bring down more distant prey.

associated with terrifying powers. The earliest ancestors attributed to the genus Homo, to which modern humans belong, is *Homo habilis*. The name hints at one of the mainsprings of human evolution – manual dexterity. *Homo*

▼ Farm workers in modern-day Egypt re-enacting ancient methods for winnowing grain.

▲ Carved in pink granite, this bust represents Pharaoh Amenhotep III of the 18th Dynasty.

◄ A scale model of an Egyptian boat used for river transport, made in around 1500 BC.

habilis literally means 'handy man' because these early human ancestors, who first appeared in East Africa around 2.5 million years ago (mya), were the first species credited with making and using tools. The names of later species in

◄ Pottery from the Danube region of Europe, dating from the Neolithic period.

▲ An ancient method of weaving, invented in around 6000 BC in the Near East and still used in South America.

◄ Pottery figure from the Jomon period in Japan, c1000 BC.

human evolution – *Homo erectus*, who migrated out of Africa and spread across Eurasia, and *Homo sapiens* – highlight two other key evolutionary factors: true bipedalism and a steadily developing brain. Over time, these developments

▼ A painted wooden model of a carpenter's workshop from the Valley of the Nobles, Thebes, dating from the 11th Dynasty.

◄ The spoked wheel of an Assyrian war chariot on a bas-relief carved at the start of the first millennium BC.

► Figure of a Mexican drummer from the 1st century BC.

◄ An alabaster cover from one of the canopic jars found in the tomb of Tutankhamun.

tempered the natural anxiety of early humans into curiosity, as people learned ways to turn nature to their advantage. The first step took place some 2.5 to 1.4 mya, when human ancestors in places such as the Olduvai Gorge, in what is

▲ A Sumerian cylinder seal and the impression it created (3rd millennium BC).

◄ A clay writing tablet engraved in cuneiform script, with a terracotta 'envelope' (c2000 BC).

▲ A terracotta jar, in a form invented by the Egyptians. Some 15 centuries later it was adopted by the Romans, who called it an amphora.

now Tanzania, began to make simple tools from flint, such as choppers and scrapers. By the Upper Palaeolithic (c40,000–12,000 years ago), a wide range of stone tools had been devised for cutting, hammering, shaping and drilling. A major

▶ A carved figure of a harpist, from around 2300 BC, found on the Greek island of Amorgos in the Cyclades group.

▲ The great Ziggurat of Ur was built towards the end of the third millennium BC.

◀ The potter's wheel, which was invented in around 3500 BC, is still in worldwide use today, as seen here in India.

innovation that made tools easier to use was the attachment of bone or antler handles to the stone blades. By the start of the Neolithic era, around 9500 BC, weapons for hunting and warfare were becoming ever more specialised and efficient.

▶ A scene from the Trojan War, showing the Wooden Horse filled with men, created in Greece in about 670 BC as decoration on the neck of a terracotta amphora.

▶ An Egyptian bronze hand-mirror dating from around 1500 BC.

▲ An ancient Egyptian farmer using an ard (an early plough), as depicted in a wall painting in the tomb of Sennedjem at Deir-el-medina, c1885 BC.

▶ A bronze statue made using the lost-wax casting method in the Peloponnese in Greece, 6th century BC.

Advances in flint-knapping and polishing stone had produced razor-sharp microlith blades and arrowheads. Another seminal discovery was the ability to make and control fire. This equipped humans with the means to cook and eat a

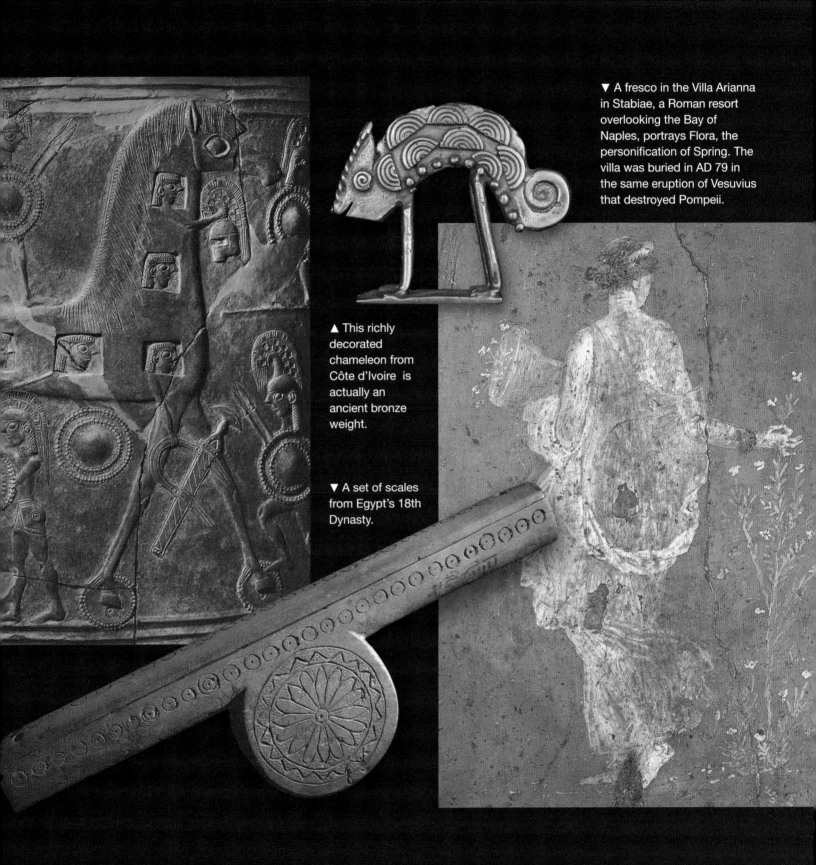

▼ A fresco in the Villa Arianna in Stabiae, a Roman resort overlooking the Bay of Naples, portrays Flora, the personification of Spring. The villa was buried in AD 79 in the same eruption of Vesuvius that destroyed Pompeii.

▲ This richly decorated chameleon from Côte d'Ivoire is actually an ancient bronze weight.

▼ A set of scales from Egypt's 18th Dynasty.

wider range of foods, making them stronger; it also enabled them to settle in colder climates. Later, fire would give rise to other key technologies, notably pottery and the smelting of metals. The development of the wheel transformed

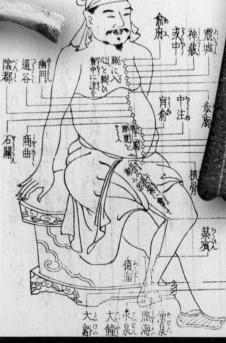

▲ A Sumerian ladle in the shape of a shell, c2500 BC.

◄ A votive statuette of Imhotep, the architect responsible for building the step pyramid at Saqqara, Egypt's first pyramid, in about 2630 BC.

► An ancient Chinese chart showing acupuncture points on the body.

transport. Global warming after the end of the last Ice Age made the cultivation of cereals possible, which promoted an increasingly settled lifestyle. Mesopotamia and Egypt became cradles of civilisation, where the first cities grew up and early

▶ A richly decorated glass flask from ancient Egypt.

◀ The Assyrian demon-god Pazuzu was believed to drive away other evil spirits, so preventing illness. This statue of him is from the 1st millennium BC.

▲ A fresco in the Valley of the Nobles near Thebes – on the tomb of Rekhmire, a vizier during ancient Egypt's 18th Dynasty – shows construction workers hauling a massive stone building block, mounted on a sled.

writing systems emerged. By 1200 BC, when our story of *The First Inventions* draws to a close, anonymous inventors and artisans had brought the human species into an age of burgeoning knowledge, trade and technological progress.

THE STORY OF INVENTIONS

This section presents the first inventions that emerged in early human history, from the Stone Age to the ancient world. Their stories have come down to us through both oral and written accounts, and through the dedicated investigations of archaeologists and other specialists in interpreting clues from the past. Both the major and lesser inventions have had an impact on society and on our daily lives, and stand as testimony to the great ingenuity of our ancestors. Here are the origins of much of our present-day knowledge and many of the tools that we still use.

The evolution of flint tools

The use of shaped flint tools is the chief characteristic of the Palaeolithic, the long era of prehistory that is known to us today as the Old Stone Age. Around 1.5 million years ago (mya), an enterprising artisan took a major technological step forward by shaping a flint tool bifacially – from both sides – to give it a vitally sharp cutting edge.

Bifacial stone tool
This piece of shaped stone (right) is the precursor of the modern knife, used for cutting, peeling, scraping or sharpening. The rounded base helps the tool to sit comfortably in the palm of the hand. Stone tools such as this enabled humans to gain mastery over their environment.

Somewhere on the grasslands of East Africa the air rings with a rhythmic sound – the noise of two stones being knocked together. Imagine the scene as a group of hominids, distant ancestors of humans, sit by a lake or on a river bank watching the toolmaker in action. In one hand he clutches a piece of flint the size of his fist, holding it steady and braced against the ground. In the other he holds a piece of harder stone, which he strikes against the flint. Every blow breaks off sharp splinters of flint. Eventually, the stoneworker holds up the results of his labour – a blade with a razor-sharp cutting edge at one end, blunt and round at the other for holding.

Technology is born

The discovery of how to make useful tools from flint, by a few intentional, directed blows, gave early man a huge advantage in the battle to survive. From this point on, humans had the capacity to make tools to help with many tasks – digging up roots, skinning and butchering animals, or carving other tools from wood or bone.

The shaping of flint tools was the beginning of all technologies. Initially, people might have picked up a stone to crack open a nut, or to throw at a scavenger. Sometimes a shard might break off and be put to good use, but once it had served its purpose, it was dropped and forgotten, just as many animals – such as chimps or crows – use tools today. The breakthrough came when an early human ancestor hit upon the idea of deliberately re-creating these chance occurrences. The combination of application and forward thinking gave rise to a method of manufacture and tools that people could use.

A human invention?

Who, then, was this proto-artisan? The early palaeoanthropologists thought it must have been an early human being, the chosen species among bipedal hominids. Such a momentous cultural advance, they argue, must have gone hand in hand with a similar quantum leap in the evolution of the species. In the Olduvai Gorge in Tanzania, Louis and Mary Leakey spent decades on archaeological digs searching for evidence of this first artisan.

In 1935 Louis Leakey found stone tools buried in a stratum or earth layer dated to around 2 million years ago. He ascribed the finds to what he called the Olduwan culture, the earliest known culture of the Palaeolithic or Old Stone Age, characterised by the use of choppers and chopping-tools. Then, on the morning of 17 July, 1959, his wife Mary unearthed a skull. Was this the missing evidence they had long searched for? Investigations eventually identified the skull as belonging to a robust australopithecine, a species thought to be earlier than human beings and closer in evolutionary terms to primates. It seemed inconceivable that the idea of deliberate tool use could have been developed by such a primitive creature.

Some years later, the logical course of evolution appeared to be restored when another discovery was unearthed in Olduvai. In 1964 Louis Leakey unveiled a new hominid to the scientific community. The skull had a cranial capacity of more than 600cm^3 – slightly less than half that of modern humans.

'LIGHTNING STONES' AND THE CONCEPT OF PREHISTORY

For many years, as the fields of Europe were ploughed, people had been turning up what were known as 'lightning stones' – curious stones that looked as if they had been shaped deliberately. No one had any concept of prehistory or Stone Age man, or even any idea how old the Earth was, and the conclusion was drawn that the stones must have been shaped by lightning strikes. This assumption was challenged in 1723 by Antoine de Jussieu, a physician and professor at Louis XIV's Botanical Gardens in Paris, who recognised that the 'lightning stones' of European fields bore a striking resemblance to stone tools and weapons made by North American 'savages'. Then, in 1800, an Englishman named John Frere wrote of finding bifacially shaped stones alongside the bones of animals known to be long extinct. Such evidence of prehistoric people using tools to hunt and butcher their kill took time to be accepted: the idea flew in the face of religious teaching. It was easier to believe in 'lightning stones'.

Look and learn
New stoneworkers learnt the techniques of flintknapping by watching an experienced craftsman at work, shaping pieces of flint using a hammerstone (above), then by practising themselves. As new methods were discovered, they would be passed on by demonstration and word of mouth.

The toolkit of
Homo erectus
The design of knapped flint tools quickly diversified, with the creation of slicers, scrapers, blades, borers and other sharp-tipped implements (above). A re-creation of a Paleolithic hand axe is shown below, surrounded by the splinters and shards of flint broken off in its making.

Well-developed masticatory muscles and teeth indicated that it was a meat-eater. The hands were equipped with more adroit thumbs, and this earned the skeleton the designation *Homo habilis* – 'handy man'. The newly discovered species was credited with all the Olduwan knapped-stone tools that had been found.

But later discoveries placed questions marks over certain assumptions. We now know that different hominid species inhabited the African grasslands in this period. In addition to *Homo habilis* and its cousin from the Lake Rudolf region, *Homo rudolfensis*, there was also the last of the australopithecines, *Australopithecus robustus* – including the one discovered by Mary Leakey. This was given the scientific name *Pananthropus boisei* (literally, 'the almost-man of Boisei'). Several species of hominids had used stone choppers – and nothing ruled out any of them as the first artisans. Even if the stone tool was not exclusive to early proto-humans, it still changed their lives, making them better equipped to exploit resources in an environment that was growing steadily drier. Meat became more important in their diet, which in turn aided their physical development – not because they had weapons to hunt big game, but because they were better able to strip carcasses that they came upon. Such activities also honed cooperation, proving the importance of working together.

Invention of the biface

The advent of tools produced an entirely new form of social organisation. Proto-humans gave up life in the trees and before long, in evolutionary terms, they emerged as the sole hominid species. Human evolution was no longer simply a physical process, it was a cultural progression. As tools and living conditions improved, intellectual capacity developed and language began to take shape.

Around 1.8 mya, *Homo erectus* appeared on the African stage. It was this early human species that discovered the beauty and utility of symmetry in tool-making: by 1.5 mya they were creating double-edged, or bifacial, stone tools which were far more effective than earlier versions. *Homo erectus* also became the first great explorer, as the species spread out from Africa, the cradle of humanity, to inhabit the Middle East, Asia and Europe. They took their bifacial tools with them and in the mid-19th century some of these were unearthed at Saint-Acheul near Amiens in northern France. Dated to around 700,000 years ago, the find gave its name to the Acheulean culture from the second era of the Lower Paleolithic (the earliest period of the Stone Age).

In addition to bifacial cutting tools, these people made cleaver hand-axes, scrapers and serrated cutting tools with saw-like teeth. Over time, toolmakers learnt that by using softer materials, such as bone, horn or wood, they could remove ever-finer flakes from a flint core, thereby creating sharper tools. Did they know how to attach bifacial blades to shafts to make stone-tipped spears? They certainly knew how to hunt large herbivores by driving them into pit-traps and killing them with spears. They would then butcher the carcasses with knives, chopping through bones with their cleavers. Larger bones, stuck in the ground and covered with dried and scraped hides, became the first tents.

Technological progress

Humans strove endlessly to improve their tools. Around 200,000 years ago, *Homo erectus* perfected the so-called Levallois technique, a method of flint-knapping that entailed striking flakes from a block of flint in a predetermined pattern to use a minimum of material. This not only indicates ingenuity, but also application – teaching and learning were clearly taking place.

But if humans were acquiring mastery over nature through the development and use of tools, they were also making more work for themselves. A skilled toolmaker could produce a basic bifacial tool in two or three minutes, but it took many hours of careful craftsmanship to produce the arrowheads typical of the Solutrean civilisation, also discovered in France, which flourished some 20,000 years ago. Shaped like laurel leaves, and with elaborate barbs, these magnificent artefacts are the work of true specialists.

Long-lasting technology
Pieced together from more than 150 fragments, this skeleton of Homo habilis *was discovered in Kenya in 1972. This hominid species, which lived around 2 mya, is noted for its skill in crafting stone tools, including primitive saws (above). The jade knife-blade (left) was made in China using biface techniques during the Neolithic era, which began around 12,000 years ago.*

FIRE – c500,000 BC

The epic story of fire

By around 500,000 years ago, Homo erectus had taken the secrets of making and controlling fire to Europe and Asia. With the mastery of fire, early humans took a great evolutionary leap forward. Fire not only offered security and warmth, but also radically changed people's eating habits and, in time, gave rise to countless other technologies.

Fire from the sky
Terrifying though lightning strikes and bush fires would have been to early humans, it cannot have been long before people tried eating the flesh of game animals that had been burned to death in natural fires – and began to realise the enormous advantages offered by the ability to control fire.

Our ancestors did not invent fire: it was a natural force that they had to contend with. Blazes could be started by burning lava from erupting volcanoes, or by lightning strikes on dry grasslands or forests and, just as for other animals, fire would have been a source of terror for early humans. What set our ancestors apart was that they recognised the advantages and possibilities that fire could offer. Overcoming fear, they tamed and domesticated fire, devising ways of containing and deliberately making it, and eventually coming up with remarkable new uses of fire.

First steps

The earliest definite evidence of fire usage is from around 1.4 mya, in Africa. Excavation of a site at Chesowanja in Kenya occupied by *Homo ergaster* (a subspecies of *Homo erectus*) has revealed several patches of charred clay. A cave at Swartkrans in South Africa has also yielded fragments of burnt bone from around the same period. But there is nothing at either site to show conclusively that these fires were started deliberately, or to tell us how they were used. An archaeological dig in northern Israel found clear traces of fire usage by humans some 700,000 years ago, but here again there was no evidence of a man-made hearth.

The first incontrovertible fire-pits, where remains of fireplaces, pieces of wood, burnt bone and scorched stones suggest intentional fire-making, date from around 500,000 years ago. Such sites are the work of *Homo erectus* and have been found as far apart as France, Hungary and China. The level of heat generated is another tell-tale sign: combustion at around 600°C indicates controlled use of fire, whereas a bush fire typically gets no hotter than 200°C.

It is unlikely that *Homo erectus* tamed fire with the primary intention of keeping warm. Fireplaces that retain heat are not encountered before the end of the Middle Palaeolithic,

around 35,000 years ago. Even then, we cannot be certain that they were made with this in mind; they might have been designed primarily for cooking. What is certain is that fire was the first source of external energy that early humans learned to exploit. It enabled *Homo erectus* to move out of the naturally warm African climate and colonise more temperate lands.

Security and light

Fire fundamentally changed the nature and pace of life. As night fell, people could settle down around a campfire, secure in the knowledge that predators would be afraid to come too near to the flames. Fire also lengthened the day: having an artificial source of heat and light meant that a tribe's activities were no longer restricted to hours of daylight. The earliest known stone lamps, fuelled by animal tallow or vegetable fats, date from around 200,000 years ago. Torches of resinous wood would have been in use from much earlier, but for obvious reasons, no evidence of these survives.

It was only a short step from the principle of containing fire within a hearth to the idea of making fire portable. A vital step in people's mastery of fire was learning how to start it at will and to keep it alight. There's no way of knowing what fire-lighting method – striking sparks with stones or rubbing sticks together – was used by *Homo erectus*. But producing a spark or glowing ember, getting a combustible material to catch and then transferring the flame from this to larger pieces of wood all call for a certain amount of ingenuity and forward planning – traits that *Homo erectus* had already shown elsewhere.

The invention of cooking

We might speculate that early humans first got a taste for cooked meat after sampling the delicious roast flesh of a deer or wild boar

trapped in a bush fire. Whatever its origin, cooking transformed people's lives. Using animal hides or leaves as receptacles, humans began to braise, boil or even steam their food. Foodstuffs, especially starchy roots and tubers, were made more digestible by cooking, and so did not weigh so heavily on the stomach. Studies of skeletons from this period indicate that from this point on, the human body absorbed nutrients more rapidly and efficiently. By feeding themselves better, our ancestors grew stronger and more resilient to disease. People's mastery of fire fundamentally altered their physiological development.

The domestication of fire also brought with it a whole new set of tasks and responsibilities. These largely devolved to women, who were now required to

Mastery of fire
Native peoples in places from Fiji (top left) to Botswana (below left) still use fire sticks and bows to make fire. The ancient firelighter (above and left) dates from Egypt at the end of the second millennium BC.

MAKING FIRE

There are two basic methods of making fire – friction and percussion. In both methods the principle is the same: the warmth or spark produced sets light to a readily flammable material.

The friction method involves rubbing two sticks of dry wood together to generate heat; the different techniques used to achieve this include the fire stick and fire drill. A fire stick is a piece of dry wood with a blunt end that is positioned in a small hollow gouged into a larger piece of wood and rapidly rotated. The friction ignites tinder – dry grass or moss – placed in the hollow. In the fire drill, a cord is wrapped around the fire stick and attached to the two ends of a bow, which is used to rotate the stick.

In the percussion method a spark is produced by striking a piece of hard stone, such as quartz or flint, against a ferrous rock, such as iron pyrite. Fragments of flint and pyrite have been found in abundance in Neolithic sites such as Star Carr in Yorkshire. Over time, the simple piece of stone was replaced by a purpose-made firelighter of a strip of flint glued with resin to a wooden handle. In the developed world, these basic techniques have been honed into the match and cigarette lighter.

CONQUEST THROUGH FIRE

First of all, fire helped early humans to extend their control over their environment. Not only did it help to drive off predators, scavengers and pests, it also enabled our early ancestors to move into the cooler, temperate zones of the planet, bringing more territory within the human domain. They harnessed its warmth to help them survive not only winters but also periods when the Earth plunged into ice ages. In the interglacials they moved further still, gradually extending human habitation into northern Europe and central Asia. Yet fire could also be deployed against other humans, and while some tribes knew its secrets, others did not. It became a means of waging war and gaining supremacy, giving people the ability to take over new lands. Burning projectiles – such as flaming arrows and blazing balls of pitch – were eventually supplanted by firearms and explosives that hurled flame and death over an enemy's lines of defence.

Blazing torches *were useful weapons against wild animals.*

Modern fire use
A foundry worker draws molten metal from a smelter, which generates the high temperatures needed for steelmaking.

extend their traditional role of foraging for food by gathering wood and other flammable material. Back at camp, it fell to them to tend the fire and cook meals on it.

Applying fire

When subject to intense heat, some rocks crack, while others shatter. Noticing this, early humans began using fire as far back as 500,000 years ago to break up large boulders or split open deer antlers. They also found that some materials responded to heat: for instance, fire hardened the points of wooden spears – in Germany three examples of fire-hardened spears have been found, dating from 400,000 years ago. Such weapons increased hunting efficiency: large game animals could be killed by spears thrown from further away, with less danger of being gored or kicked, or by constructing pit traps lined with sharpened stakes. Later, people discovered that heating with steam made animal tusks and bones more pliable, so they could be bent or straightened.

By the Upper Palaeolithic (*c*25,000 BC), craftsmen were sufficiently skilled in the use of fire to be able to prepare the pigment red ochre by heating yellow ochre to a temperature of 250°C. They also melted resin to glue shards of flint onto short, stabbing spears. Over time, people learned to select different woods to generate either heat or light, and in the absence of wood they learned to use other flammable materials such as bone, peat or dried dung.

Fire usage really came into its own during the Neolithic Revolution, which saw the emergence of agriculture (as opposed to hunter-gathering) about 10,000 years ago. With the spread of farming, people used controlled burnings to clear large tracts of land for cultivation. The era also saw the first true technical application of fire, with the firing of clay to make pottery (terracotta). Although ceramic figurines have been found from earlier eras, it was in this period that domestic pottery began to be made on a widespread basis, first on open hearths and later in ovens.

Later still, as ever higher temperatures were reached, the smelting of metals from ores began, bringing the Bronze and then the Iron Age. Today, industrial furnaces used in iron and steel smelting reach temperatures of 5,000°C or more. Fire has the ability to completely alter certain materials, bringing out truly extraordinary properties in them, and over the years the applications of fire and heat have become ever more varied and refined.

COOKING WITH HOT STONES AND STEAM

The very first cooking methods, known to be in use from the Palaeolithic era onwards, were roasting and grilling on heated stones. Later, people learned to cook in boiling water contained in goatskin flasks. Before long, early humans discovered that receptacles made of other materials such as tree bark, bamboo and the stomach-linings of animals could be made heat and flame-resistant if they were kept constantly moist, and so were good for making stews.

The technique of braising was developed by wrapping up food and heated stones in leaves, then placing them on embers and covering them with a layer of ash. The method, known as a 'Polynesian Oven', is still used in Tahiti. Steaming, a variant, involved pouring a little water into the wrapping leaves, which then immediately evaporated on contact with the red-hot stones. The Indonesian islanders below are using hot stones to cook in a ground oven.

Modern kitchen utensils are little more than adaptations of all these cooking methods dating from prehistoric times. Only the technology has changed over time: wrapping fish in foil and cooking it in an electric or gas oven is simply a modern version of wrapping it in leaves and placing it on the glowing embers of an open fire.

Timeless simplicity
With its bulbous body full of fuel, this red sandstone lamp crafted during the Upper Palaeolithic could have provided light the whole night through. Fifteen centuries later, the design of terracotta lamps had barely changed, except the rims were curved inwards to prevent spilling.

The stone lamp
c20,000 BC

The first stone lamps date from around the same time as the first cave art. Is it possible that they were devised to illuminate the cave walls for early artists as they worked? Or were they perhaps a way of keeping the paintings – which almost certainly had a ritual function – permanently lit?

The diversity of sites where ancient stone lamps have been found suggests that various groups of people hit upon the same idea simultaneously – that a small amount of oil, fat or resin could be contained in a durable receptacle and set alight. The classic shape for a stone lamp in northern Europe was a flat, oval-shaped pebble, with a dip in the centre to hold the fuel. In the Middle East large seashells were used; the shell design was retained even when materials such as alabaster and terracotta became available (below).

Whether by chance or design, people noticed that if thin twigs or strips of moss or lichen were twisted together, steeped in fat and dipped in the oil, the flame would stay continuously alight. Thus was born the oil lamp with wick.

A large number of prehistoric stone lamps have been found, made from sandstone, limestone and, less frequently, pumice. They generally used animal fat (tallow) as a fuel, and most of them were simply made from naturally hollow stones. Far rarer are those crafted by man. One of the best examples of this type of lamp comes from the famous caves at Lascaux in the Dordogne. Lying at the bottom of the so-called Lascaux 'well', excavated in 1940, were two stone lamps. Only one has survived (left), and is on display at the National Museum of Prehistory in nearby Les Eyzies. Carved from red sandstone, it is shaped like a small snowshoe, with a distinct handle that makes it easier to hold.

A PRACTICAL SOLUTION

As humans adopted a more settled lifestyle, from around 9000 BC, so there arose the need for a permanent, portable source of fire for cooking and for scaring off wild animals that threatened their encampments. The ideal solution was the pottery or earthenware lamp. Comprising a reservoir of fuel with a separate spout for the wick, they were more practical than stone lamps. This basic design was retained even when metal became the preferred material. Lamps were eventually supplanted by the tallow candle – a wick encased in hardened animal fat – which is mentioned for the first time by Roman authors during the 1st century BC.

THE SEWING NEEDLE – c16,000 BC
Perfect in one

The oldest sewing needles yet discovered made their first appearance during the Upper Palaeolithic, the most recent period of the Old Stone Age, in the time of Cro-Magnon Man (an early race of *Homo sapiens* in Europe). Items produced using this delicate tool, which was made from bone, brought great improvements in daily life. From the very outset, the invention was so perfect that in later eras the only modification to the sewing needle was the material it was made from.

Ingenious artefacts
A selection of sewing needles from around 16,000 BC (below). Drilling the eye into such a delicate bone tool demanded particular skill.

In 1921 Denis Peyrony, a French school teacher and amateur archaeologist, found an ancient bone sewing needle in a cave near the village of Laugerie-Basse in the Vézère Valley of the Dordogne. With an eye at one end and a point at the other, it was instantly identifiable for what it was. Later, in 1965, a Dr Cheynier found a magnificent specimen at a site known as the Lachaud shelter near the village of Terrasson, the only prehistoric deposit on the right bank of the Vézère. Cheynier spotted the needle lying in a pile of scree and confidently dated it as from the end of the Solutrean culture (19,000–15,000 BC). Cheynier described his find as 'the most beautiful tool I've ever come across … showing marvellous intricacy and regularity in its manufacture'.

Experts today believe that Cheynier's needle – the oldest example found so far – was made by someone from a civilisation of semi-nomadic hunters who roamed across southern Europe during the Upper Palaeolithic, leaving their traces behind them in southeastern France, Spain and Portugal. The great artistry of these people is shown in a remarkable bas-relief frieze of animals that they created at the Roc de Sers site in the Charente region and in the sophisticated bone tools that they made.

The advent of sewn clothing

This simple yet ingenious prehistoric invention combined two functions: first, it pierced pieces of material, and then it joined them together with thread. The Solutrean craftsmen who made such tools displayed incredible skill. First, a long, fine sliver was pared from a piece

Discovering ancient techniques
Contemporary archaeologists have attempted to make bone needles using the same methods as the craftsmen of the Upper Palaeolithic.

of bone using a chisel or a scraper. The sliver of bone had to be rounded and then honed to a sharp point at one end, with a blunt end at the other. Next it was polished using a small lump of fine sandstone: abrasion stones have been found with countless small grooves on their surface, evidence of repeated use in such tasks. Finally, the blunt end of the needle was pierced with a sharp piece of flint.

Sewing needles were customarily made from deer antlers, bone or ivory. Experts still disagree over whether such tools would have been strong enough to sew together animal hides. Many believe that leather, even if softened beforehand, would have to be pierced with the aid of some form of bradawl made from sharpened flint, with the needle simply being used to pull the thread through the hole. But experiments have clearly demonstrated that a bone needle is remarkably strong if it is honed to a point while the bone is still fresh.

Waterproof and warm
This hooded sealskin coat (right) was made by Inuit people in prehistoric times to gain protection from the inhospitable climate.

An all-purpose tool

The sewing needle brought great benefits to people in Upper Palaeolithic times. First and foremost, sewn skins created garments that gave them better protection from the elements than simple wraps. The thread they used was made from animal tendon or sinew, which was dried before being sliced into individual filaments and then chewed to make it pliable. A rare surviving garment from this period is a

THE FIRST TANNERS

No physical evidence remains to tell us exactly what methods were first used for softening and treating animal hides. On the other hand, several tools used in the preparation of skins – notably, various forms of scraper made from flint– have survived. Tanning animal hides, either stripped of fur or with the pelt still in place, is a complex art. It is essential to scrape off every last scrap of flesh from a hide, not only to prevent the hide having an unpleasant smell, but also to stop it from rotting and to help ensure it stays supple. Most scholars think that the first tanners used a wide range of substances – animal brains, ochre (a clayey soil containing iron oxide), and urine (extremely rich in ammonia) – to prevent hides from rotting.

Ancient technique used today
An Inuit man scrapes a caribou skin clean, just as his forebears have done for thousands of years. Caribou skins were once the standard raw material for making tents and clothing.

child's tunic made from squirrel fur, which was discovered at Grimaldi in northern Italy.

The needle also enabled people to make flasks out of animal hides, so helping them to preserve and carry liquids and other foods. Perhaps it was in this period that people first began heating sewn receptacles over fires, a major new departure in cooking methods. What is beyond dispute is that the needle was the catalyst for the invention of tents and also boats, such as the kayak, made from hides stretched over a framework of branches.

Expeditions to the Arctic in the early 19th century led archaeologists to compare the sewing techniques of the Inuit people with those of prehistoric man. Among the Inuit, the use of needles made from bone or ivory is common, using thread made either of reindeer tendons or seal entrails. With these tools, they create clothes and small boats from animal skins. The needles use by the Inuit, however, are more sophisticated than those of their ancient forebears.

History of needlecraft

From the Magdalenian culture of the Upper Palaeolithic onwards (*c*18,000–10,000 BC), needle use became widespread. In Egypt, from around 4500 BC, new materials – first copper, then bronze and silver – replaced bone. The Egyptians perfected their surgical techniques using this tiny instrument to carry out suture procedures.

In ancient Greece the needle was such a commonplace item that it crops up in a wholly unexpected context: in a fable attributed to Homer an army of mice marches off to war brandishing bronze needles as lances. On a more serious note, the embroiderers of Phrygia (in western Anatolia, in present-day Turkey) were renowned throughout the Mediterranean world for the quality of their needlework. By Roman times, sewing needles made of iron were familiar household items.

Iron needles were still in widespread use in the Middle Ages, although from 1370 onwards polished steel needles were manufactured in Nuremberg in Germany, using a technique brought back from Syria by the Crusaders. The steel needle spread throughout Europe during the Renaissance. It was reputedly introduced into England by Catherine Howard, the fifth wife of Henry VIII. Later, in the 18th century, an entire industry developed in Birmingham around the manufacture of steel needles.

Needlework became something of an art form in the making and decoration of clothes, and also in creating fine lace, such as Alençon

ALL SET FOR SURGERY

If animal skins could be stitched together for clothing, then why not sew the skin of living humans back together to heal wounds? An invention that went hand in hand with the eyed needle – thread made from animal products – soon brought improvements to primitive surgery. Indeed, thread made from animal products is still in use today, with only minor changes, in the form of catgut. Despite the name, catgut is actually made from the treated and sterilised intestines of sheep and pigs (sometimes mules). The original word was 'kitgut', meaning 'fiddle string', which was coined in the 16th century when the same material was used to manufacture the strings of several instruments, including the violin, cello and harp.

lace from Normandy. Needles from the factories of L'Aigle in Normandy became world-famous, rivalling those made in England. Even the revolution in the clothing industry brought about by the invention and spread of the sewing machine in the 19th century failed to dent the prestigious reputation of expert hand-needleworkers. Some 18,000 years after its invention, the sewing needle remains an indispensable tool in the hands of high-fashion professionals around the world and in domestic use in every home.

Sewing a boat
An Inuit fisherman repairs his boat using methods passed down through many generations.

Straight or curved
Some 3,000 years ago, the ancient Egyptians not only made weaving shuttles (below), but also curved needles (left), or awls, for sewing clothing from animal skins.

How prehistorians reconstruct the past

O nly a tiny number of pieces of physical evidence have survived to tell us about the distant past. Piecing the bits together to reconstruct the way in which our ancestors lived often resembles a police investigation, and the complexity of the task increases the further back in time we go.

Neither chance nor intuition, *but long hours of study and painstaking research in libraries are what lead archaeologists to investigate particular sites. Here, a researcher in SCUBA gear is lifting pots from the wreck of a ship that foundered off the coast of the British Isles in 1205.*

Above all, researching prehistory involves teamwork. Physical scientists (geologists, sedimentologists, palaeontologists) must join forces with social scientists (archaeologists, ethnographers) and specialists in the life sciences (biologists, molecular geneticists) to pool their knowledge and expertise.

Not much to go on

The prehistorian's task is hampered right from the outset by one big problem: lack of data. After a million or so years, all organic matter has completely vanished and any bones that survive will have fossilised. Even for later periods, finds are few and far between: jaw fragments, bone splinters or knapped flints. Fortunately, the occasional extraordinary find can help to fill in some of the gaps, such as the marvellously preserved dugout canoe found in a peat bog at Pesse in the Netherlands in 1955, one of the oldest boats ever discovered (c8000 BC). Or, even more incredible, the 5,000-year-old traveller known as 'Ötzi' who came to light intact in the Ötztal Alps in Italy in 1991, found frozen into a glacier complete with clothing, tools and weapons!

Searching with a fine-toothed comb

Excavations are often carried out using small scrapers and fine paintbrushes, and the first task of archaeologists is to locate, note and carefully remove as many pieces of evidence as possible: hearth stones, cinders, spoil heaps left behind from flint-knapping, bone fragments. Even the positions in which items are found may provide scholars with vital clues.

The finds are then analysed in a laboratory. Studying tools under an electron microscope, for example, enables scientists to determine when they were last used. Analysis of rocks and metals can reveal exactly where they came from. Examining teeth reveals much about the diet of early hominids. Bone analysis can bring to light weaknesses in physical make-up or damage resulting from accidents during a person's daily life. Complementing this work are studies such as the analysis of pollen and dendrochronology (dating trees by studying their growth rings), which can reveal a great deal about the prehistoric environment.

A never-ending puzzle

Every discovery helps to fill in another piece of the jigsaw and gain more insight into the lives of our remote ancestors, including their spiritual world. But every answer serves only to prompt further questions. One mystery concerns the hundreds of paintings in the famous Chauvet Cave in the Ardèche region of France, which show predators such as lions, panthers, bears and hyenas rather than the more usual paintings of game animals that would be hunted. Interpreting these images as dream symbols, some scholars have speculated that prehistoric humans saw caves as portals into the spirit world. Modern examples of shamanism have also been studied for points of comparison. Only one thing remains beyond dispute: the study of prehistory is not a science that deals in certainties.

Meticulous groundwork
Once the site has been carefully marked out with a grid and photographs taken, the basic spadework of archaeology can begin, using trowels and paintbrushes, as here at the Klaises River in South Africa. At some particularly fragile sites, such as the Altamira Cave in Spain (inset), archaeologists work from a complete virtual reconstruction.

DATING METHODS

Scientists have an array of techniques for dating their finds. The following are among the most commonly used:

• Radiocarbon dating:

This method is based on the decay of radioactive atoms over a given period of time (the 'half-life'). The atoms of each element have a half-life specific to that substance, so this acts, in effect, like a clock. When a living organism dies, the clock starts ticking. We know that the half-life of the naturally occurring radioisotope carbon-14 is 5,568 years. By measuring the reduced ratio of carbon-14 atoms to regular carbon atoms in a sample, we can count back in units of 5,568 years to date the sample. Carbon-14 cannot be used to date artefacts beyond 50,000 years, but other radioisotopes – such as uranium-238, which has a half-life of 4.47 billion years – can be applied to dating older artefacts.

• Thermoluminescence:

This dating method is based on the discovery that certain crystalline minerals that are 'charged' with natural or artificial radiation emit light signals when later heated. The stronger the light signal emitted, the older the sample. Thermoluminescence can be used to date ceramics, for example, as these become radioactive during firing in a kiln.

TRIAL AND ERROR

Researchers are always keen to try to reproduce prehistoric working methods, as this allows them to assert or discount certain hypotheses. For instance, scientists who have tried making bifacial tools have realised just how skilled a task it was to remove fine flakes from a flint core. This has led them to conclude that flint-knapping specialists who served long apprenticeships must have been a feature of the Upper Paleolithic (35,000–10,000 BC) and beyond.

A weapon for hunting and war

Devised for hunting some 12,000 years ago, the bow and arrow made all other animals on Earth – whether on land, in the air or in water – potential prey for humans. Some 7,000 years later, the bow became a standard weapon of war that was only supplanted by the advent of firearms. Since Tudor times, the bow and arrow has enjoyed a civilised role in the sport of archery.

Eight thousand years *separate the bowman in this painting at Tassili n'Ajjer in the Algerian Sahara (c6000– 4000 BC) from the modern-day hunter opposite, but the weapon is the same. The modern hunter is Aman Baoi, a medicine man on Siberut, an island in the Mentawai archipelago of Indonesia.*

It is not known for sure when or how the bow and arrow came into being. Flints in the shape of arrowheads from the Upper Palaeolithic have led archaeologists to surmise that it may have arisen among the last hunter-gatherer peoples in around 10,000 BC. In the same period, rock paintings in the Araña cave complex in southern Spain show hunters drawing bows to shoot prey, while similar images from the Niaux caves in France portray a bison wounded by an arrow.

A new way of hunting

The Early Neolithic period was the heyday of the hunting bow. As the Earth warmed after the end of the last Ice Age, the environment started to change. By this stage, humans had acquired technical skills in making microliths – tiny stone tools or blades, which could be attached to arrows as barbs. A bow could be used to bring down all kinds of animals, and it became the favoured mode of hunting. Arrows were superior to spears in almost every respect – speed, power, range and accuracy. In Northern Europe the main prey animal was reindeer, while further south, along the Atlantic coast, people hunted forest animals such as wild boar, red and roe deer, and rabbits. Hunting with spears and spear-throwers needed a large group, with separate parties of beaters and throwers. The bow put a premium on spotting and tracking an animal, and on stealth in approaching it.

A range of weaponry

Neolithic hunters employed a wide variety of arrows suited to different game. Some were sharply pointed, others had a chisel-like cutting edge, others still were barbed – equipped with a series of sharp points down one or both sides – or honed to a razor sharpness with miniature flint chiselling tools. To bring down birds or small mammals, the hunter would use an arrow with a club-shaped bulge at the end instead of a flint head, so as to stun the prey without damaging it. This kind of arrow is still used by Inuit peoples today.

The bow and arrow that was developed at the start of the Neolithic was technically very accomplished. The earliest bows were

Formidable arsenal

Hooked and barbed harpoons and a spearhead (near left) from the Upper Palaeolithic (c17,000–11,000 BC). At close quarters, such weapons were highly effective against large prey. Later, the hunter's arsenal was augmented by a range of small flint arrowheads (far left) that were capable of hitting prey from a distance; these examples date from around 6000 BC.

HUNTING AND FISHING TECHNIQUES

Around 10,000 BC, when the bow first appeared, the arsenal of the Upper Palaeolithic hunter comprised a range of different weapons: the boomerang, the short stabbing spear and spear-thrower (atlatl), the javelin and the harpoon – a spear with a detachable barbed head. Hunters also dug pit traps to catch large game, and set snares for birds and small-girth animals such as rabbit and young wild boar. Sometimes, people would take domesticated dogs hunting with them. Meanwhile, fishing, which is known to have been practised from at least the Upper Palaeolithic onwards, developed further during the Neolithic, as fishermen began to use harpoons, javelins and the bow and arrow to catch pike and salmon. Smaller fish were trapped in nets; fragments of ancient nets made from plant fibres have been found in lakes in Finland and Estonia. Throughout Europe, Neolithic man used a wide variety of hooks made from bone, shell or boar's teeth. Floats made from tree bark and stone weights discovered at Starr Carr in Yorkshire are the precursors of modern fishing tackle, along with the long keep-nets woven from willow roots and branches found at the same site. Although modern sport hunters and fishermen have equipment made from state-of-the-art materials such as carbon fibre, they are still basically using techniques that were first developed in prehistoric times.

roughly the same height as a man and constructed from a single type of wood. Some Neolithic bowmen wore small plates of shale or bone fixed to the wrist with thongs to prevent the skin from being rubbed raw by the bowstring. The earliest evidence found of a bow and arrow in use are pine arrow shafts dating from 8500 BC discovered at Stellmoor near Hamburg. Excavations at Bercy, outside Paris, have unearthed a Neolithic bow in good condition, dating from *c*4600 BC. The weapon is made of yew, a resilient yet pliable wood often used for bows; it is 1.54m long and shaped following a simple, symmetrical curve. Alongside it were arrows measuring 70cm tipped with flint arrowheads. The Bercy bow is one of the oldest yet found in Europe.

FROM HUNTING TO MUSIC-MAKING

Some palaeontologists think that early man may have first got the idea for a stringed instrument from the resonant twang made by a bowstring as it was let go. With the addition of one, then two, then several strings, plus a sound box, this may have been the origin of the lutes, lyres, citterns, harps and guitars that were developed over the centuries that followed.

Warriors and hunters
All three images here date from the 6th century BC. The famous fresco of archers (above) is from the palace of Darius, ruler of the Persian Achaemenid Empire, at Persepolis. The mounted archer who inspired this bronze statue was probably Scythian (right). Although the bow became a weapon of war, it continued to be used for hunting, its original purpose, as shown in the lion-hunt scene on this Persian cylinder-seal (left).

MYSTERY OF THE ICE-MUMMY'S KIT

Certain features of the equipment found with Ötzi, the famous 5,000-year-old ice-mummy from the Ötztal Alps in the Italian Tyrol, have puzzled archaeologists since they were uncovered in 1991. When Ötzi came to light, the objects he was found to be carrying included a chamois-leather quiver, but the bow that was lying next to him – a simple yew bow, 1.82 metres long – is clearly unfinished and looks more like a staff than a weapon. A lime-bark cord found in the quiver is believed to be the bowstring. The quiver contained 14 arrows with viburnum and dogwood shafts. Only two of these still had their flint arrowheads, glued on with birch tar and held in place by animal

tendons. The feather flights were also attached with birch tar and tied on with fine plant fibres. The 12 remaining arrows were unfinished shafts, about 80cm long, with notches cut in their ends ready for heads to be mounted.

The bow and arrows were not all that Ötzi was carrying: he had a wood and flint dagger and a copper-bladed axe, as well as various tools made from wood, antler and flint. It is unclear whether all this was the equipment of a hunter, a shepherd who carried such items to defend himself and his flock, a traveller crossing inhospitable terrain, or a man fleeing attack. What is certain is that the weapons had seen considerable use before Ötzi died; it appears that he had dropped his bow, and his arrows were damaged. Death overtook him before he was able to repair his vital kit.

The bow in the Near East

The bow and arrow also formed part of the hunter's arsenal in Mesopotamia. Unlike subsistence hunting, hunting for sport – or as practice for war – was the preserve of the king and the ruling elite in Assyria and Babylon. Reliefs depict archers in chariots hunting lions, onagers and aurochs (an ancient, now extinct, species of wild cattle). Special arrowheads were made for the royal game hunts, usually triangular and with razor-sharp edges designed to make an animal lose a lot of blood and tire quickly.

In Egypt the bow, along with the javelin and the club, was one of the oldest known weapons. The nobility used it to hunt aurochs, gazelle and wild sheep in the desert. The ancient recurve bow used by the Egyptians was relatively short, rarely exceeding 1m. The recurved shape is clearly visible in the hieroglyphic pictogram for 'bow'. The arrows, made of bulrush stems, were on a similar scale, measuring only 50cm. Arrowheads made of several different types of material have been found, including flint, agate, fish teeth and ivory. Some extremely sharp arrowheads were coloured red; this may have signified that they had been dipped in poison, or perhaps it was part of a magical rite, whereby the red of the arrowhead was supposedly drawn to the animal's red blood.

The Egyptian bow evolved down the ages. In the Old Kingdom (from c3000 BC) the straight-limb bow appeared, measuring anything up to 1.7m. Subsequently, this took on a new shape: the bow commonly deployed in the New Kingdom (from c1570 BC) was a less unwieldy composite bow, made of thin strips of wood bonded together. Among the various hunting or military artefacts placed as grave goods in the tomb of Tutankhamun, there are several bows and arrows, as well as a wood and copper bow case richly decorated with gold-leaf panels depicting hunting scenes.

Object of veneration
No arrow was ever fired in anger from his 16th-century Cambodian bow. Made of bronze, it was impossible to draw, and was used purely for ritual purposes.

Fearsome killing machine

By the end of the Neolithic, the bow and arrow had become a weapon of war. Following the advent of metalworking, arrowheads made first from bronze and later from iron became ever more deadly. Around 5,000 years ago, the Sumerian army already boasted one detachment of archers and one of lancers. As the *Epic of Gilgamesh* records: 'And now they brought to them the weapons, they put in their hands the great swords in their golden scabbards, and the bow and the quiver.'

Thereafter, right up to the 15th century, archers were involved in almost all military campaigns. In ancient Egypt, the bow and arrow was the standard-issue weapon for the army, while warrior-pharaohs were trained to fire at distant targets from light, horse-drawn chariots (the only other weapons of this period that could hit a target at 100–200m were the sling and the boomerang). Other notable exponents of archery in warfare were the Assyrians, the Persians, nomadic peoples from the Central Asian steppes – notably the Goths, Huns and Scythians – and last but not least the Mongols, whose light, manoeuvrable cavalry was renowned for devastating the enemy with a hailstorm of arrows. Their prowess as mounted archers is unsurpassed. In Europe, at the Battle of Crécy in 1346, the French cavalry was cut to pieces by English and Welsh bowmen: using longbows made of yew, oak or maple, they could fire over a distance of 200m at a rate of 10–12 arrows per minute. Even at the end of the Middle Ages, despite competition from the crossbow, the longbow still played a key role in warfare. Its lightness, the ease with which it could be deployed and its greater range gave it an edge over its newer rival. Yet the bow and arrow proved increasingly ineffectual when faced with firearms, and the 16th century saw its demise as a weapon of war in Europe.

Raw power

Manufacturers of modern bows consider the straight-limb Mesolithic bow an almost unsurpassed design. Nowadays, this type of bow is still widely used by sport hunters. Bowmakers usually craft them in a single piece, often from fine, supple, expensive woods such as box or maple.

Modern archery equipment makes use of the latest technology. The limbs of compound bows are made from composite materials, such as wood and glass fibre or carbon ceramic (CCM), while the strings are Dacron or Kevlar. Carbon-fibre or aluminium-carbon arrows have replaced wooden ones and fibre-optic technology is used to make the sights for competition bows. Some bows have cams mounted on the ends of the limbs to increase the archer's draw weight while reducing the force that has to be exerted.

Archers without quivers

Placed in the tomb of the Egyptian general Mesehti some 4,500 years ago, these archer statues carry their arrows in their hands, even though quivers were familiar equipment by then. Likewise, the 15th-century artist who painted this scene of the siege of Jerusalem (above) omitted to depict quivers across the archers' shoulders.

Modern bows

A Japanese yabousame, *or mounted archer, draws his bow and shoots at full gallop during a demonstration in London (right). Bows made for archery competitions (far right) display both exquisite craftsmanship and cutting-edge technology.*

39

A versatile tool

For prehistorians, the appearance of the polished axe marks the transition from the Palaeolithic – the Old Stone Age – to the Neolithic. The axe played a major role in the shift from a hunter-gatherer lifestyle to forest clearance and farming.

Symbol of power
The advent of the polished axe, like the one held by this Sumerian warrior (above), or those brandished by the Bronze Age figures in the petroglyph below, signalled the dawn of a new era.

Somewhere in northern Europe, a forest rings with a cacophony of sounds: men grunting with exertion and calling to one another, stone axes chopping into tree trunks, the sharp crack and dull thud of a tree being felled. Between about 3900 and 2800 BC, in the temperate region that later became Denmark, human settlers hacked out clearings in the vast Nordic forest to grow cereals. These people were the first European farmers and also the first to built permanent settlements.

The forest was far more than just a hindrance to be felled to clear land for cultivation – it furnished the settlers with the ideal material for building their homes. A whole industry grew up as skilled artisans turned out flint axes by the hundred. If the flint found on the surface was scarce or of poor quality, they sunk wells up to 15–20m deep to get at underground seams of the precious material. This was the genesis of northern Europe's first mines. And the polished axes that Neolithic man produced were in constant use. At several lake and riverside sites, the fossilised remains of birch, ash and pine trees still bear the marks of axe blows. These same marks also crop up elsewhere – in the tunnels of ancient flint mines, for instance, on the walls of Neolithic burial chambers in the Marne Valley in northern France, and even on the skulls of some of the bodies interred there.

The art of polishing stone

The Mesolithic Natufian culture of the eastern Mediterranean (the Levant) is credited with inventing the art of stone polishing in around 10,500 BC. Several non-functional items, such as elongated pendants and batons, have been discovered at the Tell Mureybet site in Syria. The first polished stone axes also came from Palestine, some 2,000 years later.

Making an axe required considerable skill. First, the craftsman carefully chose a block of stone, such as flint, diorite, or serpentine, knocked the roughest edges off it, then shaped it using a hammerstone. Thus far, the process was identical to that employed since the Palaeolithic era. Little by little, the blade was sharpened by chipping off flakes to create a cutting edge. This preliminary work produced a long, thin axe-head. The process of getting the axe-head smooth then began. The craftsman would rub the object on a polishing stone – a rough block of soft sandstone with deep grooves cut in it – while wetting it at regular intervals. The water and fine stone dust combined to form an abrasive paste that gave the tool a polished surface and honed the edge. A hole was then knocked through the heel of the axe to take the haft.

Onerous yet effective

The ultimate aim of this lengthy and laborious procedure was to make a long-lasting tool that was fit for purpose. The polished stone axe had the advantage over its predecessor that it could be recut and repolished if it got broken or chipped, or sharpened when it became blunt. Ethnologists studying the Kim Yal people of New Guinea in the 1990s can attest

Polished stone
These smooth axe-heads dating from c5000 BC (above) were found in the Gulf of Morbihan in Brittany. Tools like this are still used by the peoples of Papua New Guinea to make dugout canoes (far right). In Bronze Age China, axe-heads like the one shown here were cast from metal.

to the effectiveness of such tools: using just their stone axes, the Kim Yal can cut down a tree the girth of a telegraph pole in under 10 minutes. The fact that stone-polishing techniques were still being practised by such tribes in the late 20th century enabled palaeontologists to confirm their ideas of how axes and other polished stone tools were manufactured and maintained in the Neolithic.

With the rise of metals, people in the Middle East and Europe gradually abandoned the polished stone axe in favour of bronze axes. The metal-headed axe was further refined during the Iron Age and has remained largely unchanged ever since.

THE NEOLITHIC TOOL KIT

The polished stone axe, the essential tool of early foresters and builders, has become the quintessential symbol of the Neolithic. Yet a number of other tools made in the same way also appeared at around the same time. Derived from the axe, which has its blade in line with the haft, the adze has a blade set at right angles to the haft and was used for smoothing rough-cut timber or for digging. Also, stone sledgehammers not dissimilar in shape to axes have been found at some riverside sites, prompting

archaeologists to surmise they were used to drive the corner posts of log cabins into the ground.

To harvest crops, farmers used sickles and reaping knives with curved or straight blades. The cutting edges were made from razor-sharp strips of stone set into a handle. Once harvested, grain was ground either in a mortar made of polished stone (or sometimes wood), or with a millstone usually made from a flat or convex stone. Some Neolithic millstones had a pitted grinding surface to give them better traction on the grain.

Finding more power

A little over 35,000 years ago, humans learned that by adding handles to their flint tools they could greatly increase the force exerted by their hands and arms, and thus make many of the tasks they performed easier or more efficient. Following this realisation, they developed tools that remain among the most familiar in use today, including the hammer, axe and chisel.

Spear-throwers *were developed in the Upper Palaeolithic. They increased a hunter's throwing power tenfold (below and far right) and became highly prized objects. This exquisitely decorated spear-thrower (right) was found at the Mas d'Azil site in the Ariège region of the French Pyrenees.*

The advent of the spear-thrower (atlatl) revolutionised hunting. This wooden device, with a notch at one end, enabled hunters to hurl spears with greater force and accuracy, making it easier to target prey that was larger and farther away. Of even greater importance was a new type of hunting spear that made its first appearance sometime during the so-called Aurignacian culture (*c*32,000–26,000 BC).

The new weapon was a sharp-pointed throwing spear, but unlike its all-wooden predecessors – which were useless once the point became worn down or damaged – this spear had a replaceable tip made from reindeer antler or bone that had been attached to the wooden shaft. The spear itself was in two parts, with the sharp end mounted on a wooden haft. Composite weapons like this were lighter than earlier spears – in skilled hands, the new spear could kill a large deer grazing at a distance of around 80 metres. Above all, the new spear was more practical, as a broken point or shaft could be replaced without having to make a whole spear from scratch.

A new range of tools

From around the start of the Neolithic period (*c*12,000 years ago) in Europe and the Near East, a new range of sophisticated composite tools began to appear. They comprised a haft, usually made of wood, into which were set small pointed or sharpened pieces of flint or bone, known collectively as 'microliths'. Microliths were used to tip arrows for

MAKING MICROLITHS

Microliths are small flint tools, some measuring no more than a few millimetres across. To make such tiny tools, the artisan would begin by cutting two notches on the edge of a thin flint blade. Using these as guides, the blade was then snapped across its width to create a triangular microlith. The residual pieces of the original blade from above and below the microlith were known as microburins (literally 'tiny chisels'); these were often discarded, but sometimes used as finishing tools. After polishing, the microlith would be attached to a handle (right). Microliths were also made in other geometrical shapes, such as trapezoids, or half-moons ('lunates').

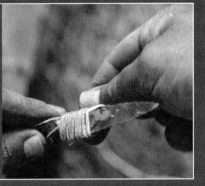

hunting birds and small game, and were also incorporated into grating implements or knives. One of their 0advantages was that they were replaceable. As the technology evolved, the haft of the tool began to determine its form and function. Primarily, handles made tools easier to hold and manipulate. As the use of handled tools spread, people learned how to position themselves more comfortably while working, and how to carry out tasks with greater ease and economy of effort.

Composite tools also helped to refine fishing techniques. Harpoons from the Magdalenian culture (*c*16,000–10,000 BC), for instance, are highly complex weapons. As soon as the harpoon struck home, the removable head came loose from the shaft and embedded itself in the animal, which unless killed outright would struggle and flee. The hunter kept hold of a cord made from leather or plaited strips of plant fibre, the other end of which was attached to the harpoon head; this allowed the hunter to follow and control the wounded prey.

Mounting the cutting end of the harpoon onto the rest of the shaft was an extremely subtle business: the harpoon head, usually made of bone, had to fit snugly into the haft so the two pieces did not part company when the harpoon was thrown. The trick was not to make the fit too tight, as there had to be sufficient play to allow the head to detach at the right moment.

Hatchets
The tool on the left is from the Neolithic, while the other two were made in modern-day rural Indonesia. The basic principle is the same for all: the longer the handle, the greater the power.

Agricultural implements

The oldest farming tools yet found date from the Neolithic period, *c*8,000 BC onwards. They come from riverside and lakeside sites in the Swiss cantons of

Amerindian hatchet
Made by the Anasazi people of southwestern North America, this 11th-century hatchet comprises a head made of polished stone tightly lashed to a willow-branch handle.

SYMBOLIC HANDLES

Ever since flint blades were first mounted on handles, humans realised that the length of the haft changed the way that a particular tool should be used. The basic principle was the longer the handle, the greater the force that a tool could exert. Anthropologists believe that this explains the emergence – in areas of the world as far apart as Asia, Oceania and the Americas – of ceremonial hatchets with impractically long handles. Clearly not for normal use, the sheer length of the handles marked such tools out as high-status ceremonial objects belonging to chieftains.

A VARIETY OF FIXING METHODS

Even during the Magdalenian culture, there appear to have been different methods of fixing handles to spears. For example, light single-bladed spears were made by lashing the blade onto the top of the handle, whereas double-bladed spears had the blade embedded within the handle. The thin flint blades of knives sat in a groove specially carved into the wooden haft. Resin made from plants or animal by-products, such as birch bark or fish oil, were used to cement the fixing and make the whole tool stronger. Implements used for hitting usually had a recessed or morticed handle into which the head was embedded to absorb the impact. By contrast, hatchets had a hole drilled through the head itself, with the handle set into it, a technique that is still used for axes today. More sophisticated fixing methods began to spread from the end of the Neolithic period. For instance, before being fitted to the handle, the blades of hatchets or adzes would be sheathed in a sleeve of wood or antler, which helped to absorb the impact of blows and also reinforced the handle. Even in these improved tools, cord bindings and glue were still used to strengthen the bond.

Fribourg and Neuchâtel, and from the Jura region of France. The finds – complete tools as well as detached handles – show that in addition to knives, scrapers and harpoons that differed little from ancient versions, the first farmers had new tools such as machetes, hatchets and adzes made of polished stone to help clear ground for cultivation, as well as picks to loosen soil and knives for harvesting.

These pioneers learned how to use the properties of different woods to best effect, finding out by trial and error whether a handle was best made from pine, ash, honeysuckle or apple wood. By using natural forks in trees, or branches whose odd shapes lent themselves to making implements for specific tasks, they also invented tools with angled handles.

Hard to beat

In their seminal *Encyclopédie* of 1751–72, the French Enlightenment thinkers Denis Diderot and Jean d'Alembert listed and illustrated several examples of tools in use for many thousands of years. Contemporary engineers then set about trying to improve them – and failed. The design of ancient hatchets, knives, adzes and pickaxes was perfectly matched to their function, and the only improvements that could be made were in the materials used or in minor details. Even today, despite using the latest, most durable and reliable materials – such as cold-tempered steel, carbon steel or glass fibre – the basic form of tools has changed very little.

A science of subtle signs

A relatively recent scientific discipline known as traceology has given archaeologists new insight into ancient tool use. By studying the surfaces of tools at various levels of magnification, prehistorians have found marks invisible to the naked eye. From these, they have been able to reconstruct the precise kinds of movement made with particular tools – such as rotative, transverse or longitudinal motions. This data enables researchers to work out whether a tool was used, say, for stripping skins off carcasses, or for slicing through bones, wood or meat. Traceology has identified fish scales on flint blades, even when no other fish remains have been found at a site. By studying the degree and type of wear and tear, scholars can tell whether a tool or weapon was heavily used, whether it originally had a handle, and even whether the person who once wielded it was right or left-handed.

Scaling sheer heights
A rock climber uses ice-picks with highly sophisticated carbon-fibre handles to grapple her way up the face of a frozen waterfall.

The comb c10,000 BC

The first known combs, made of bone and dating from around 9000 BC, were found in ancient burial sites in Scandinavia. Through the ages, the comb became an indispensable fashion accessory for both men and women. In ancient Egypt, combs supplanted long needles as a way of keeping unruly hair in place.

Egyptian combs were made from ivory, wood, sometimes even gold, and often had teeth on both sides. As well as being useful everyday implements, they were also regarded as decorative luxury items. A comb from the early 18th Dynasty (14th century BC), found in the necropolis at Deir-el Medina and now on display in the Cairo Museum, is decorated with the ankh symbol – the Egyptian 'cross of life' – with an image of the falcon-headed god Horus and a bird's wings. In ancient Rome, combs tended to be made of boxwood, bone, ivory and, occasionally, bronze. Several fine examples were excavated from the ruins of Pompeii. In his 'Edict on Maximum Prices' of AD 301, the Emperor Diocletian fixed the price of a comb at 14 denarii.

In such a straightforward technology, the main thing that has changed over time is the material of which combs are made. Tortoise-shell combs were first produced in America in the mid-18th century, while the celluloid comb, precursor of the plastic comb, first appeared at the end of the 19th century. Plastic combs, which were easier to manufacture, are now much more common than metal ones.

From practicality to vanity
Iron Age bone carding combs (above) epitomise the practical aspect of combs, but they also came to be associated with luxury and vanity. The illumination below from the 'Angers Apocalypse' tapestry of 1373–87, shows the Whore of Babylon preening herself with the aid of comb and mirror.

Objet d'art
Though primarily a functional tool for combing wigs, in ancient Egypt the comb became an art form in its own right. This comb decorated with an antelope motif was made in around 1500 BC.

THE ADAPTABLE COMB

Since it was just as useful for untangling fibres as hair, the comb came to play a key role in weaving from the first appearance of the horizontal loom in around 3000 BC. Equipped with hooked iron teeth, the comb became an indispensable tool for the wool carder. It was also used to tighten and smooth the weft strands as a piece of cloth was being woven. So-called 'rippling combs' were used to strip away the seed husk from hemp and flax and prepare the fibres for weaving.

Over the course of history, farmers have found other uses for combs. The Gauls in particular used them at harvest time to separate ears of corn and other cereals from their stalks.

Sailing the oceans and discovering new continents

From makeshift craft designed to help people to fish or to cross small stretches of water, boats gradually developed into sturdy ocean-going vessels that would carry people, trading goods, wealth and ideas from nation to nation. The ship was soon harnessed as a means of waging war, and during the European 'Age of Discovery' it conveyed explorers, conquerors and adventurers to new lands.

Early forms of boat *invented in the Neolithic and still in use today include the bamboo raft (seen left in the Solomon Islands) and the long, narrow, flat-bottomed dugout canoe – the example below is from the Mentawai Archipelago on Sumatra. Intriguing though it is as an artefact, the schematic representation of a Viking ship and its crew (above) yields little information about boats of the period.*

Tried and tested technique
A Peruvian man and his son building a boat for use on Lake Titicaca in the High Andes. Their ancient technique involves lashing together bundles of plaited reeds. The 'Kon Tiki' expedition mounted in 1947 by the Norwegian ethnographer Thor Heyerdahl proved that reed boats were perfectly seaworthy on the open ocean.

The earliest, rudimentary attempts to take to the water would in all likelihood have involved people simply sitting astride felled tree trunks and paddling to propel them forwards. Such makeshift craft would have been virtually impossible to steer and in constant danger of turning turtle. Over time, the problem of instability was overcome by lashing together several trunks or bunches of reeds (depending on what materials were to hand) to create a larger and more stable platform – the raft.

Early purpose-built boats

The first purpose-built boats were dugout canoes and the most ancient example found to date was discovered in Holland. Carved from a pine log, it dates from between 8200 and 7600 BC. Still in use in places like Amazonia, dugouts were hollowed out using stone axes or adzes, and were propelled by various means. In shallows, they were punted with a pole, while in deeper waters, paddles were used. A wooden paddle from *c*8000 BC has been found at the Mesolithic site at Starr Carr in North Yorkshire. Other early types of boat probably resembled the traditional coracles of Wales (or

SHIPBUILDING TECHNIQUES

The most fundamental elements in the construction of a wooden ship's hull are the keel – the main structural member running the entire length of the ship at its lowest part, from bow to stern – and the knee, a curved piece of wood that joins the keel to the stem. On an ancient ship, the sternpost – the counterpart of the stem at the rear of the vessel – supported large oars set on both port and starboard sides, which served as rudders.

The section of hull below the waterline was made up of transverse members attached at their lower end to the keel; at the upper end the transverse members were attached to crossbeams, supported by braces rising from the keel. The beams supported the deck, which first appeared in around 1500 BC on Phoenician ships. The external sheathing of the hull was of planking, which was

secured to the transverse members in the framework of the vessel.

In modern naval architecture, the first steps in building a boat are to lay down the base of the hull (the keel, stem, sternpost and braces), before sheathing the vessel. In ancient times, the process was reversed: first, the planking was assembled using pieces of timber joined either in clinker-built fashion (that is, overlapping one another like the tiles on a roof) or carvel-laid (with the planks butting up against one another, edge to edge and held in place with pegs). All the components designed to strengthen the hull were then put in place. Caulking – a technique whereby the joints between planks are sealed with bitumen or pitch to ensure that the hull is completely watertight – was invented around 3000 BC in Mesopotamia.

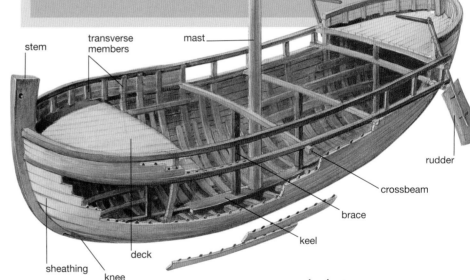

Ancient shipbuiding techniques

The components that made up the hull of an ancient vessel are shown on this reconstruction of a Roman cargo ship prepared by the Museum of History in Marseilles, France.

the curragh of Ireland) and the kayaks of the Inuit, which are made by stretching bark or animal skins over a light wooden frame.

In the absence of wood, the ancient Egyptians used papyrus reeds from the banks of the Nile to build basic rafts. Later, they were the first to devise true shipbuilding techniques: bulrush stems, split into thin strips, were joined together to create a kind of planking that was used to form the hulls of boats. Meanwhile, in Mesopotamia, an abundance of

The ancient Egyptians *powered their vessels by sail from c3000 BC, but as the fresco above shows, oars were still used alongside the new method of propulsion. The sail seems to have been mainly used on seagoing vessels of the period. The scale model boat from c1500 BC (right) was propelled solely by means of oars and so was of a design mainly used for river transport.*

livestock made goatskins an obvious choice of material to build rafts for use on the Tigris and Euphrates rivers. Tied side by side, inflated skins provided buoyancy and the rafts could be used to carry heavy loads. The circular, basket-shaped craft known as the *guffa*, which can still be seen in Iraq, is the direct descendant of ancient Mesopotamian river craft.

The invention of the sail

Oars were the most basic means of propelling a boat, but people soon came to realise the potential of a piece of canvas set to catch the wind. The sail may have been invented by Pacific islanders in around 6000–5000 BC. Around that time, Polynesian peoples

are thought to have begun using triangular sails made of plaited strips of bark or wood on their outrigger canoes – two dugouts joined by poles to form a catamaran. But the discovery of a sailing ship in a tomb dating from around 5000 BC in the Sumerian town of Eridu suggests that the sail appeared in several parts of the world at around the same time.

Ancient Egyptian ships pictured on frescoes and vases had a very distinctive long profile, with both the prow and stern rising high out of the water. The single central mast supported a sail that was tied to the hull by lanyards. This meant that the sail could only be used with a tailwind. The boats were steered by two oars mounted at the stern.

In around 2500 BC, Egyptian expeditions up the Nile brought back with them not only precious supplies of wood from the south, but also new boatbuilding techniques. They began to make boats with flat-bottomed hulls by joining small planks of wood together with pegs. The mast, which from now on was sited amidships, carried a sail as wide as the boat was long, which improved wind resistance in open waters. The sail itself, made from woven canvas, could be angled slightly using strong lines of twisted rope and was unfurled whenever favourable winds arose. When running against the wind, the ship was powered by oarsmen deployed along either side of the vessel. Ancient Egyptian ships like these were light and manoeuvrable, but poorly adapted for navigating rough seas.

In search of stronger hulls

It was the Phoenicians, in around 1500 BC, who first strengthened the hull with transverse beams and by a brace running along the centreline of the vessel – the keel. Made of several lengths of timber joined together, the keel formed the backbone of the ship. Phoenician vessels were 10–20 metres in length and known as 'round ships' from their pot-bellied appearance, which made them more stable. They could be manned with a crew of just three or four men, and because they were powered purely by sail, they no longer needed to weigh anchor at night to give oarsmen time to rest. Before long, this type of ship was in service in merchant fleets the length and breadth of the Mediterranean, and would continue to be used for more than 1,000 years.

The Romans perfected the round ship, stretching it to more than 30 metres in length and adding a greater area of sail. They were also the first to clad the hull in sheets of lead to ward off the ravages of the teredo shipworm, a saltwater mollusc with a taste for ship's timbers.

Lugsails, lateen sails and square sails

But for all their advantages over earlier designs, Phoenician ships remained unwieldy. It was master mariners from later cultures, starting with the ancient Greeks, who were to develop faster, more manoeuvrable vessels.

Square-rigged ships were severely hampered by only being able to sail when the wind was blowing directly from astern. This problem was overcome in the 3rd century BC with the advent of the lugsail – an asymmetrical

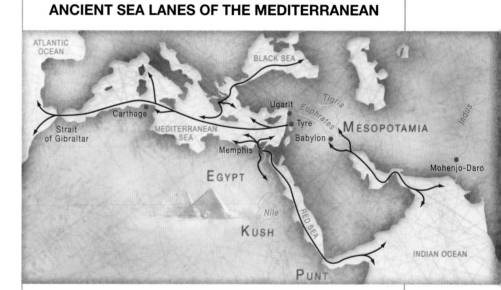

ANCIENT SEA LANES OF THE MEDITERRANEAN

Trade has always been the prime mover in forging links between peoples. The Mediterranean, the Nile and, further east, the River Indus (on whose banks a remarkable civilisation arose from c2350 BC, around the city of Mohenjo-Daro) were key ancient routes for transporting people and goods and spreading cultural influences.

As past masters in the art of river navigation, the ancient Egyptians later ventured onto the high seas, reaching the coast of Crete in around 3000 BC. Around 500 years later, they began to explore the southern lands of Kush and Punt (on the borders of modern Sudan, Eritrea and Ethiopia), bringing back timber, resin, ivory and gold, and establishing regular trading links with the region. In around 1300 BC, Pharaoh Ramesses II ordered the building of a canal to link the Mediterranean with the Red Sea. Work on this

forerunner of the Suez Canal was abandoned in the 8th century BC, but the waterway was finally completed by the Persian king, Darius I, in the 5th century BC.

The thriving city of Ugarit on the Syrian coast in the eastern Mediterranean was an entrepôt not only for the produce of the entire Mediterranean region, but also for amber from the Baltic. Trade in iron from Cyprus stimulated the growth of arms manufacture, for which Ugarit became famous. By the 8th century BC, the Phoenician civilisation based here and at other ports of the Levant was firmly established as the main maritime power in the Mediterranean. The Phoenicians set up trading posts along the North African coast, and in c1000 BC became the first traders known to pass through the Straits of Gibraltar in search of silver, lead and tin from northwestern Spain and as far away as Cornwall in Britain.

four-cornered canvas. Lugsails were mounted directly along the longitudinal axis of the ship, with the top attached to a spar (or yard) that was hoisted up the mast. The arrangement enabled sailors to alter the angle of the sail and so take advantage of crosswinds.

From the lugsail, the lateen sail, which was triangular in shape, developed. The new sail became widespread throughout the Mediterranean at the beginning of the Middle Ages. Lateen sails are still used on Arab vessels such as dhows and feluccas.

Further innovations came from cultures beyond the Mediterranean. In Scandinavia, the Vikings – superb sailors – invented the square sail in the 8th century AD. Being completely movable, the new Viking sail could take advantage of winds from any direction.

More sheets to the wind

Meanwhile, the Chinese, whose technical expertise would later amaze Arab and European seafarers, had already put multiple masts on their vessels to increase the total sail area that could be deployed. They equipped their sailing ships, known as junks, with several longitudinal sails: the number could be varied according to the winds. In the Middle Ages, the dissemination of knowledge that followed in the wake of increased trade brought about a synthesis of all these elements. The result was the three-master, which began to appear in the 15th century, using squaresails and lugsails. The 19th century saw the culmination of this development, as the sail area of ships increased to extraordinary proportions. In the case of some tea clippers, it reached over 3,000 square metres.

The traditional steering-oar, as used by the Egyptians, was of limited effectiveness because it was located off the vessel's centre-line. It was gradually supplanted by the stern-mounted rudder, which had been invented by the Chinese as early as the 1st century BC but was not adopted in Europe until the end of the Middle Ages.

Advances in ship design

Galleys and their later variants (galleasses, galiots, brigantines and fustas) formed the backbone of Mediterranean fleets right up to the 17th century. Their earliest ancestors were Cretan and Carthaginian vessels, which combined sail-power and oars. In turn, these gave rise to the Greek trireme, the quintessential longship of ancient times, which was used both for trading and as a warship. The triremes were armed with a fearsome ram on the prow, and were propelled by several banks of seated oarsmen, in addition to one or more square sails.

In Northern Europe a type of ship called the nef was developed, which in time took on various new guises, including the carrack (influenced by Saracen ship design) and the cog. The carrack, which was used for both trade and war, was replaced at the start of the 16th century by the galleon, a massive, heavy vessel that was extremely sturdy but not very manoeuvrable. During the European 'age of discovery' of the 15th and 16th centuries, the need for custom-built ships capable of long voyages gave rise to the caravel, a sleek sailing ship built for speed and equipped with multiple masts carrying every kind of sail.

Even so, these long-distance ocean voyages would have been impossible but for the invention of new navigational instruments. The astrolabe dates from the 2nd century BC, the magnetic compass came in the 12th century AD and the Portolan chart at the end of the 13th century, with nautical dividers shortly thereafter.

Mighty clipper
Sail technology reached its peak in the ocean-going tea clippers of the late 19th century. The four-master pictured above crossed the Atlantic in just two weeks in the 1850s.

Nile feluccas
Arab sailors invented the lateen sail in the 3rd century AD. It can be swung through an angle to allow the vessel to sail 'closer to the wind', so the wind does not have to come from directly behind to make good headway.

THE FIRST WARSHIPS

Warships and battles at sea have taken place almost as long as commercial seafaring. According to the Greek historian Thucydides (c460–400 BC), the ancient Greek trireme – a warship driven by both oar and sail power, and equipped with a ram on the prow that made it a formidable weapon – was invented by Corinthian carpenter Aminoklis in around 700 BC. By that time, the Egyptians had long had a fighting fleet. The mortuary temple of Ramesses II at Medinet Habu (c1176 BC) includes depictions of ships involved in a naval battle against the 'Sea Peoples' (probably the Phoenicians) who were ravaging the Delta during that period. The fighting ships were in all likelihood very similar to the merchant vessels that plied the waters of the Nile.

FARMING – c8000 BC

From a nomadic to a settled lifestyle

From around 10,000 BC, groups of human beings progressively abandoned their nomadic way of life based on hunting and gathering to live by farming instead. The development brought with it a radical transformation in the way people lived and fed themselves.

After the end of the last Ice Age, in around 11,000 BC, the Earth's climate gradually began to warm up. The change stimulated the spread of several plant species that until then had been rare or even unknown. Wild cereals sprang up across the grassy steppes of western

Asia, in an area that became known as the 'Fertile Crescent', but it is impossible to give a precise date for the first appearance of agriculture. Even before the invention of cultivation as such, people would have picked and used the ears of the wild grain, following the tradition of gathering that had characterised their way of life for some 50,000 years. Some experts reckon that it must have taken at least 4,000 years for Neolithic people to move from an economy based on hunting to one based on production. There were many stages to be mastered: finding and preparing ground suitable for cultivation, the gathering and reliable storage of grain, the cycle of

Seasonal rituals A 21st-century farmer would have no difficulty in identifying what is going on in this ancient Egyptian fresco of rural life from 2,500 years ago. It shows the cycle of ploughing, sowing, harvesting and transporting the harvested crops.

A clay model of an Egyptian granary dating from around 2000 BC (right).

sowing and harvesting. There is documented evidence that the first harvests occurred in various regions of the world between about 8000 and 6000 BC, with barley and wheat being grown in the Near East, sorghum and millet in Africa, and maize in Mexico and Peru. Somewhat later, millet and rice made their first appearance in China. From these initial pockets, agriculture developed apace as land was cleared for cultivation. What has been termed the 'Neolithic front', in which farming practices spread into new areas, advanced on average by one kilometre a year. In this way, over the course of 3,000 years, various strains of wheat which had origins in the Near East spread into Europe.

Wild versus cultivated cereals

In wild cereals, the ears detach easily and disperse of their own accord – natural strategies that help to ensure successful propagation. Moreover, the grains of wild grass species are small and, most importantly, 'husked' – that is, they are covered with a solid glume (coat) which protects the seed until it takes root. These characteristics are to the plant's advantage in the natural world, but they turned out to be drawbacks to the people who wanted to cultivate, harvest and eat them.

Initially, the Neolithic gatherers must have had to make do with the few ripe ears that stayed in place on wild grasses and did not disperse. It was these atypical, or mutant, grains that were the first to be cultivated: without being conscious of it, early humans proceeded to select a gene pool for primitive cereals. As a result, the wild wheat varieties that were cultivated in the Fertile Crescent – wild emmer or einkorn – were selectively bred

over many generations, going through a series of hybridisations and transformations. The process, which must also have involved cross-fertilisation with other kinds of grain, eventually led to the appearance of 'naked' wheat varieties, in which the grains were stripped of their husks and therefore easier to winnow and eat.

The improved wheat went on to be cultivated in thousands of different varieties. Cultivated varieties proved more disease-resistant, richer in nutrition (as they had a higher gluten content) and easier to harvest. On the downside, they lost the capacity to reproduce without human intervention and so the price that humans paid for a continuing, reliable source of food was to be tied to a settled farming lifestyle.

A brand-new diet

People of the Palaeolithic, or Old Stone Age, were predominantly big-game hunters and carnivores, while those of the Neolithic, who had learned how to farm, made cereals their staple foodstuff and their primary source of protein. To begin with, wheat, barley or millet were eaten raw: clear evidence of this has been found by archaeologists examining early human remains in which the teeth show striations and abrasion associated with the lengthy chewing of grains that were hard to separate from their husks.

Experimentation with cooking – possibly just by throwing grains onto red-hot stones – represented a major advance, as cooking converts the starch in the grains into sugars. This increased the nutritional value of cereals considerably, since sugars are easily assimilated by the human intestine, whereas digestive juices have difficulty breaking down raw starch. Here again, the study of early human skeletons has provided achaeologists with confirmation: when the cereals are eaten

Ancient equipment
This millstone and grinding stone provide evidence of flour production in the Finisterre region of Brittany, north-western France, from around 4000–3000 BC.

PANCAKES AND BREAD

What were the key stages that marked the route from hunter-gatherers chewing raw wild cereals for sustenance to the baking of the first bread?

The first step was undoubtedly the development of naked varieties of wheat or barley that would have made it easier to thresh the grain (separate the grains from the ears) and to winnow it (separate the edible grain from the chaff). Once this had been done, the grain could be ground down into flour on a millstone. The flour, either roasted or left plain, was mixed with water to produce gruel, or made into unleavened pancakes that were simply cooked on hot stones over a fire.

The gradual evolution of different sorts of wheat played a key role in the long history of bread. As cereals underwent genetic changes, wheat became more gluten-rich which gave it new characteristics, since higher gluten made flour more suitable for making leavened bread. Archaeologists have identified Predynastic Egypt, where the oven was already in use, as the place where leavened bread was first made. Perhaps its genesis was in a peasant family, where a young daughter making flat bread became distracted from her work and left her mix of flour and water from the Nile standing in the hot sun. A few hours later, she would have gone back to find a swollen dough that, once baked, produced a light, risen bread. Quite by chance, natural yeasts in river water gave rise to the world's first leavened bread. Over the succeeding centuries, bread has remained the staple diet of many people on Earth.

roasted rather than raw, the wear on teeth is less – but on the other hand, the first signs of tooth decay appear as a result of eating sugars.

Greater variety in foodstuffs went hand in hand with improved farming practices. From about 7000 BC, the cultivation of staple cereals in the Middle East was augmented by leguminous vegetables. In Anatolia, and later in Europe, people added lentils and then peas to their main diet of wheat. In China, soya beans were grown alongside rice and millet, while in Mesoamerica, the potato and the tomato enriched a diet based on maize. All these innovations resulted in a more varied and desirable range of foods. At the same time, from around 7000 BC onwards, earthenware receptacles became more widespread, initially in the Middle East and Anatolia. These

Baker's boys
A clay model dating from c2000 BC (above) shows two ancient Egyptian bakers in the process of making bread.

Neolithic life
Settlements like the one below in modern-day Ethiopia have been a feature of this region since the very earliest days of farming.

promoted more effective storage of food and were also useful in cooking.

Towards a settled lifestyle

We cannot be sure what precisely induced the hunter-gatherers of the Palaeolithic to give up their traditional diet. It may have been an increased scarcity of big game, or an upsurge in the population coupled with a change in the climate. What is certain is that the ability to schedule harvests from one season to the next radically transformed the way people lived. Wherever a settled way of life was adopted, it is associated with a major growth in population. People reorganised themselves first into communities and then into villages. Over time, some villages evolved into towns, then city-states and kingdoms, thus generating the need for administrative structures – in other words, forms of government.

THE GROWTH OF IRRIGATION

The cultivation and expansion of farmland entailed a series of complex tasks – clearing ground, ploughing and sowing, storing grain from one season to the next – that would have been inconceivable without strong collective organisation. The first settled communities were established in the most favourable locations, close to rivers, where rich alluvial soils promoted crop growth. And yet agriculture remained precarious: a spell of low rainfall, or conversely a flood, could be enough to trigger food shortages. It soon became apparent that the survival of communities depended on effective water management. In the Middle East, where the presence of the Tigris and Euphrates rivers had encouraged people to adopt a settled lifestyle, the newly evolved city-states took steps to regulate water use: the first irrigation scheme may have involved diverting a tributary of one of these rivers. From early in the 3rd millennium BC, Mesopotamians were building terraces, drainage culverts and irrigation canals controlled by sluice gates. In Egypt, reservoirs to store water from the Nile's annual flood helped to expand the area of land under cultivation. Later, the Romans used irrigation extensively in their North African provinces. Meanwhile, in northern China, terraces were carved out of the loess soils of the Huang He (Yellow River) valley to protect crops from being washed away when the river broke its banks.

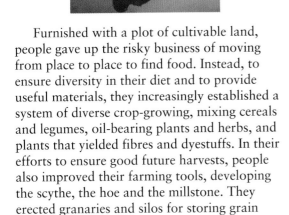

Furnished with a plot of cultivable land, people gave up the risky business of moving from place to place to find food. Instead, to ensure diversity in their diet and to provide useful materials, they increasingly established a system of diverse crop-growing, mixing cereals and legumes, oil-bearing plants and herbs, and plants that yielded fibres and dyestuffs. In their efforts to ensure good future harvests, people also improved their farming tools, developing the scythe, the hoe and the millstone. They erected granaries and silos for storing grain

Old methods today

The technological advances that transformed agriculture in the 19th century bypassed many regions of the world where ancient farming methods are still employed. This granary (right), depicted in an Egyptian model from around 4,000 years ago, would not look out of place amid the modern rice-growing terraces of China (above) or in the irrigated fields of Sudan (inset left).

Cow transport
A mural of c2500 BC shows boats being used to move cattle on the Nile.

A LATE DELICACY

The chicken today is the world's most popular and widespread domestic fowl, but it was one of the last animals to be domesticated by humans. The ancient Egyptians discovered it at the end of the 13th century BC, describing it as the 'white meat bird'. They imported it from Syria, which itself had acquired it shortly before from India, where the jungle fowl was first domesticated in the 15th century BC.

Domesticated deer?
Found in Mesopotamia and dated c2000 BC, a painted relief carving appears to suggest that deer were once domesticated there.

during winter, and learn how to make durable receptacles for cooking food in various ways.

The domestication of animals

Since it was impossible for settled farmers to go off hunting for long spells, they began instead to keep animals close by. The practice of livestock husbandry arose at roughly the same time as agricultural cultivation.

The earliest forms of animal husbandry are thought to have developed in the Near East around the middle of the 9th millennium BC. People constructed rudimentary enclosures for herds of goats or wild sheep, which were then exploited for their milk and fleeces, as well as for their meat. In Mesopotamia, the domestication of goats and sheep is known to have predated that of pigs, which occurred in around 7000 BC, and cattle (c6500 BC).

It also appears that, quite early in human history, certain animals were domesticated for purposes other then food. The first creature harnessed by humans is thought to have been the dog from around 12,000 BC onwards – probably much earlier. Dogs descended from wild canine species such as wolves, coyotes or jackals are believed, for example, to have been raised and domesticated by Amerindians in what is now Idaho in North America, almost certainly to help them hunt. Meanwhile, in the Near East, the domestication of cattle stimulated other developments: following the invention of the plough in around 3000 BC, cattle effectively became draught animals. In the same period, the Chinese grew mulberry trees and learned to cultivate the silkworm; at much the same time, beekeeping began in Egypt and llamas were domesticated in the High Andes of South America. Domestication of the wild horse was relatively late, thought to have first been achieved by people of the Ukrainian steppe in around 4000 BC.

HUMAN IMPACT ON ANIMALS

In choosing particular animals to domesticate, humans played a direct role in the evolution of certain species and the extinction of others. From the wolf, the ancestor of all canids, humans bred dogs as diverse as the Basset hound, chihuahua and Pomeranian Spitz. Yet people also contributed to the extinction of the dwarf elephant, which still thrived in North Africa in c1000 BC, and dwarf hippopotamus, which roamed southern Europe some 10,000 years ago.

Bitumen

*c*7000 BC

Bitumen is a mix of various hydrocarbons, in a more or less solid form, which is found naturally in abundance wherever there are petroliferous (petrol-bearing) rocks. The sticky black substance bubbles up to the Earth's surface in various places – on the right bank of the Euphrates, close to the Sumerian city of Hit; on the Bahrain archipelago; and on the banks of the Dead Sea. The Greeks named this last site 'the asphalt lake'.

A useful substance

Ancient peoples of the Near East were quick to recognise the potential benefits of bitumen, both in its semi-solid, malleable state (in which it could be moulded into flat pancakes for ease of transport), and in its more viscous, liquid state, when it was known as naphtha (from the Akkadian *naptu*) and stored in leather flasks or earthenware jars. The usefulness of bitumen soon became apparent to the Mesopotamians and Egyptians. But while the latter used it primarily in the mummification process to conserve corpses, the Mesopotamians found many applications for it. For instance, applied in several layers, it was used to fix in place the bricks that paved the processional ways in ceremonial cities such as Babylon. In a similar way, it was used to waterproof roofs, terraces

Ceremonial goblet
Made of bitumen in around 2000 BC, this artefact from the city of Elam (in modern Iran), has survived almost undamaged.

and the base of walls, as well as receptacles and jars. It was used for caulking boats, especially vessels made from bundled reeds – a practice that continues among the Marsh Arabs of Iraq. Mesopotamian apothecaries mixed it with other substances to make poultices for people suffering from rheumatism or pleurisy; such formulae survived long after the Arab conquest of the Middle East in the late 7th century AD. Finally, Sumerian and Egyptian artists used it as an adhesive to fix inlaid materials – such as mother-of-pearl, bone, ivory and precious stones – onto items of furniture and sculpture. Bitumen is still used for roofing felt and in road-making, as well as in certain varnishes employed in etching.

BITUMEN AND PHOTOGRAPHY

Natural bitumen – or 'Bitumen of Judea' as it was known – played a key role in the invention of photography. In 1822, a French pioneer of photography named Nicéphore Niépce took the world's first known photograph using a pewter plate coated with bitumen, which turns white when exposed to light. The bitumen-coated plate was placed at the back of a camera obscura, in which a small pinhole had been cut to form the lens.

Bitumen and boats
Caulking – waterproofing between planks with bitumen – is still practised today, as here in Jamaica.

The creative urge

The findings of palaeontologists confirm that people have long felt the desire to adorn their bodies, to beautify their ritual and ceremonial sites, and to decorate their living spaces. The fruits of this creative drive were countless decorative artefacts, displaying a plethora of designs on different materials. Taken together, these early creative endeavours form the basis of what later became known as art.

Some 30,000 years ago, at Grimaldi in Italy, a group of early humans buried one of their dead. The man's body was carefully laid to rest dressed in all his finery, with his head draped with a net made from tiny seashells. The corpse was covered with a layer of powdered red ochre, while around it were placed all kinds of grave goods – votive offerings, tools and arms. When the grave was discovered by modern archaeologists, the first thing they unearthed was the man's skull, with the net still intact, its mesh held together by the shells.

In the same period, the so-called 'Sungir Man' was buried in Belarus, clothed in garments onto which had been sewn hundreds of tiny ivory discs made from tusks of the woolly mammoth. Although the fabric itself had not survived the passage of time, the discs had remained in place, covering the man's skeleton from head to toe and indicating that his corpse had been dressed for burial in a cap, mittens, jacket and shoes.

Body ornaments

A seashell necklace dated to around 75,000 years ago has been found in a cave in South Africa, but most palaeontologists today agree that body ornamentation probably became widespread towards the end of the Middle Palaeolithic, c30,000–40,000 years ago, with late Neanderthal and early Cro-Magnon man. These early human species used natural pigments to decorate their bodies with symbols. They also selected seashells, mammals' teeth and small pebbles, both to

Prehistoric jewellery
These fragments of bone and shells (left) are the remains of a necklace once worn by an unknown woman from the beginning of the Neolithic era in the Marne Valley in France. The gold ornaments below belonged to a wealthy Sumerian woman from the city of Ur, who lived some 2,500 years ago.

Early tattooing
A stamp from Colombia, South America (left), dating from around 2200 BC, which was used for printing decorative designs on the body.

Lascaux horse
Cave art, such as this famous mural in Lascaux in southern France (c15,000 BC), almost certainly fulfilled a ritual purpose that is now lost to us.

wear as pendants and to adorn their clothes or their hair. But it was in the Upper Palaeolithic that this type of ornamentation came into its own, prefiguring the ritual body art practised by many different ethnic groups worldwide, as well as the modern taste for make-up and jewellery. In this way, people proclaimed their cultural identity, the clan they belonged to, and their marital and social status. Several millennia later, following the mastery of metals in the Near East, copper and gold were worked into delicate brooches, pins and rings, while glass was smelted and transformed into decorative artefacts such as vases.

Cave art

At some stage towards the end of the last Ice Age, around 11,000 BC, a group of Cro-Magnon people ventured into a cave complex at Niaux in the Ariège region of the Pyrenees. In the shifting light cast by the torches they carried, one of them at least was evidently struck by the pattern of lumps and hollows on a section of the cave walls, especially a small, round depression in the rock, which the early artist chose for his first drawing. The hollow itself became an eye, while the head of a bison was chiselled out of the stone around it. Some 13,000 years later, the same bison, looking astonishingly modern, still gazes down at us. The location of the engraving was chosen with

care, both as regards its position in the cave and the particular quality of the rock there. To highlight certain features and bring them into relief, parts of the rock face were roughened beforehand. Sometimes, this scoring itself forms the outline of the design.

After the discovery in 1940 of the Lascaux caves in France, which date from the Magdalenian culture around 15,000 years ago, or those at Altamira in northwestern Spain, Europe became the hot-spot for cave art. Then,

REINTERPRETING CAVE ART

For a long time, the prevailing view of cave art was that it was either purely decorative or that it played a symbolic role in hunter-gatherer societies. Animal drawings were thought to have been a way of gaining power over prey, supposedly casting a spell over game prior to a hunt. A closer examination of the evidence has called this interpretation into question. For instance, it is known that the inhabitants of the Lascaux caves lived mainly on reindeer. But most of the cave paintings there show red deer; reindeer hardly feature at all. Scholars now incline to the view that cave art was associated with religious or magical rites, with its precise meaning reserved for a select few. Given our general lack of knowledge about the culture and lifestyle of these people, the significance of their art remains even more obscure.

Cave of the hands
(background)
The Cueva de Los Manos in Argentina is named after the stencilled images of hands that cover the cave walls. They were made around 9,000 years ago.

Skilled engraving
Aside from its great antiquity, the antler horn below – from the end of the Upper Palaeolithic, some 14,000 years ago – is remarkable for its realistic depiction of animals and the subtle shading technique employed by the artist.

in the 1970s, explorers such as the Frenchman Michel Siffre found other extraordinary caves at several sites in Central America: at Poxté, Jovelté, Pusilha and Canchacan. Along with the Palaeolithic site at Chauvet in southern France, which came to light in the early 1990s, these later finds have revealed that people were creating art long before the Magdalenian period – as long ago as 30,000 years and more.

The beginnings of painting

Stone Age artists were proficient in the use of both watercolours and oils, adding either water or animal fat to dry pigments to bind them. They devised sophisticated techniques, such as shading or gradations of colour, to add texture or a three-dimensional quality to drawings. They knew how to render perspective by sketching one animal in front of another, a ploy also used to create an impression of great herds and to impart a sense of movement to a scene. Early artists were also familiar with stencilling: one of the commonest images is of a human hand, created by painting around it to produce a negative outline.

These same techniques come to the fore even more prominently in the Magdalenian culture. Fingers, hands, brushes and pads made from animal skins are among the many methods used to apply either black and white or polychrome pigments to the cave walls. In some cases, liquid paint was held in the mouth and blown out in a fine spray, a method that prefigured the modern techniques of airbrushing or spray-painting with aerosols.

The most striking features of the cave art at Lascaux and Altamira are not the techniques used but the scale of some of the paintings – 4 metres long in the case of the mural known as the 'Cow with the Collar' – and the fact that the images are often in the most inaccessible parts of the cave complex. At Lascaux, no fewer than 17 traces of scaffolding have been found in clefts in the rock. Yet the discomfort artists must have experienced in working in these tight corners in no way compromised the boldness of line evident in the drawings.

Figurines and monumental art in stone

In Palaeolithic Europe, cave art appears to be a more highly developed art form than sculpture in the round. Even so, the continent's prehistoric caves have yielded several beautiful examples of animals moulded in clay, such as the bison found at Tuc d'Audoubert in the French Pyrenees. Yet the most remarkable sculpted objects of the Palaeolithic are the first representations of humans – the so-called 'Venus figurines'. These

EXPERIMENTING WITH PIGMENTS

A wide spectrum of colours is evident in rock art, ranging from black and brown to yellow, red and white. The study of pigment fragments from Lascaux – found either on the rocks themselves or on the remnants of pots and mortar – has greatly enhanced our understanding of the artistic techniques. More than 100 examples of black pigment have been found, comprising mainly manganese oxide; when mixed with other minerals, this oxide produces a palette of shades ranging from olive-grey to deep black. Yellow pigments derive from ochre (a compound of clay and iron oxide), and produce a wide range of hues from pale lemon to a vivid tan. Red pigments were obtained by heating yellow ochre. White came from kaolin (china clay). These raw minerals were pulverised with stone pestles in a variety of makeshift mortars – little hollows in rock, cavities in large animal bones, or large seashells. The resulting powder was then mixed with other mineral or vegetable pigments, or with bone ash. Finally, a binding agent, such as water or animal fat, was added.

miniature, highly stylised statuettes of women with big breasts and buttocks have been unearthed at sites from western Europe to Siberia. Bas-reliefs of animals and of sculpted tools occur in both Europe and Mesoamerica, such as stone spear-throwers made either with graving tools and stone chisels or by abrasion.

Sculpture in the round was particularly prevalent in the ancient Egyptian and Sumerian civilisations thanks to their possession of copper and bronze tools, which enabled them to work the stone efficiently. Metal points, square chisels and drill bits – all of which were invented in the Bronze Age – have scarcely changed since. The difficulties facing stonemasons in Mesopotamia were considerable. Given that stone was scarce, even completely non-existent in certain areas, their task involved transporting huge stone blocks – probably by boat – to the sites where buildings and monuments were to be erected. Mesopotamian sculpture introduced a new realism to scenes showing animals and people, subjects that had already been depicted on a small scale on cylinder-seals. Sculpted artefacts, sometimes decorated with shells or even semi-precious stones, were generally installed as votive statues in temples or used to embellish royal palaces in the cities.

Earth mother
Although the obesity of the figure is disconcerting to the modern eye, the famous Venus of Willendorf (left) would once have symbolised great plenty and fertility. The figure dates from around 24,000 BC.

Strikingly modern
This stylised cat's head in terracotta (left), made at the beginning of the Bronze Age, would not look out of place in a modern art gallery.

Carved antler *(right)*
Dating from some 14,000 years ago, this beautifully carved object is embellished with intricate geometric carvings. We have no idea what it was used for.

61

Mother and child
Stylised art features in ancient cultures all over the world. This figure of a woman breast-feeding her child is from the Jalisco period of Central America (around 1st century AD)

Earthenware as art

The art of ceramics, or fired clay, developed from around 11,000 BC onwards, initially in Japan and thereafter in Sumer, reaching Africa in around 7000 BC. A significant advance was made in the technological development of pottery around the end of the 4th millennium BC, with the invention (first in Egypt and then in Mesopotamia) of glazing. The process involved coating an object with slip (liquid) clay mixed with minerals such as lead, potassium silicate or sodium. Thereafter, pottery treated in this way was no longer porous, like terracotta. Furthermore, glazing opened up new decorative horizons for artists.

It was just a short step from here to the development of vitreous glazes. Potters began to make beads, rods and complex designs from blobs of vitreous glaze, which they used to embellish artefacts, including funerary objects. The invention of perfectly clear glass, in around 1500 BC, gave craftsmen a perfect material to make vases and decanters, and initiated a manufacturing process that has lasted for thousands of years.

Growing sophistication

Artistic endeavour covered a wide spectrum of activities, from architecture to metalworking, from mosaics to bronze-casting. Some 6,000 years ago, the Sumerians devised a new technique for decorating their buildings: the polychrome mosaic. Initially, the main purpose of the decoration was to protect the building itself – the universal building blocks of the region were fragile bricks of dried clay. The external face was covered with terracotta cones, the bases of which were painted with vivid colours, or embellished with fragments of coloured stone. The cones came to be arranged in geometric patterns, inspired by woven mats or fabrics used for wall hangings.

An Indian bronze statuette, the Dancer of Mohenjo-Daro, has the distinction of being the world's oldest known lost-wax casting. This important artistic technique originated in the Middle East in around 3000 BC, as the growing vogue for jewellery and expensive statuettes led metalworkers to devise a method of casting that could produce work of great intricacy. The lost-wax method is still used today for small-scale castings.

The first musical instruments

Music is probably as old as the human race itself. We cannot be sure when the first musical instruments were made, but it is clear that by the Upper Palaeolithic, people had already learned various ways of making music, including bone whistles, gourds filled with seeds (ancestors of maracas), and graters, which were scraped with sticks or pieces of bone to produce a rasping sound.

In the Neolithic, the simple whistle gave rise to the flute, which was usually made from a bulrush but sometimes from a long hollow bone or even from terracotta. The same period saw the appearance of the slit drum, made from a section of hollowed out tree trunk with skins stretched over the ends, as well as the prototype of the xylophone, comprising pieces of wood (bamboo in Asia) of varying thicknesses that produced lower or higher notes. There was also the mouth-bow, strung with a reed stalk; one end of the bow was put in the mouth, which acted as the resonating chamber. From this developed the first primitive zithers, strung with several 'strings', although such instruments were not known to the early civilisations of the Americas.

Blue period
A pottery vase from Egypt, made in the 14th century BC. The decorative motif represents the lotus, a sacred plant in ancient Egypt.

DO ANIMALS HAVE AN AESTHETIC SENSE?

The most famous example of an animal with a sense of colour is the bower bird of Southeast Asia. To attract a mate, the male bird decorates his ground-built nest with as many blue objects as he can gather: flowers, butterflies, other birds' feathers, man-made blue objects, such as wrappers or beads. Before starting the courtship ritual, the male bird shows his nest to a potential mate. If she signals approval, he is encouraged in his efforts and further embellishes the nest. To investigate this bird's extraordinary habit, animal behaviourists conducted an experiment: while a male was absent from his nest, they replaced the blue objects with identical ones in red. On returning to the nest with the male, the female immediately attacked him and made off, clearly demonstrating a preference for the colour blue.

MUSIC AND DANCE IN ANCIENT EGYPT

No musical notation or theory has come down to us from ancient Egypt, yet depictions of instruments and musicians suggest that music, song and dance played a central role in both sacred and secular life. From the Old Kingdom *c*3000 BC onwards, music was played in the home and was regarded as a mark of refinement. By the Middle Kingdom (2040–1640 BC) it was established in religious settings. As the range of instruments increased, ensembles appeared.

Orchestras accompanied temple rites and ceremonial processions of statues of gods. In the royal palace, the pharaoh surrounded himself with gifted musicians who composed and performed music for the court. Several attained high status and were granted the privilege of building their own mortuary temples. One such was Khufu-ankh, a 'singer, choral conductor and court flautist' in the Fifth Dynasty, who was interred close to the Great Pyramid of Khufu (Cheops) at Giza. Musical education took place in institutions linked to the palace or in special schools. Great households also maintained small orchestras and troupes of dancers for banquets and festivals. Yet music was by no means the preserve of the rich and leisured classes. It was part of working people's lives, played at family gatherings and military service. Ancient murals show scenes as diverse as a shepherd playing a flute, women beating tambourines to scare birds, and musicians and dancers accompanying the harvest and grape-picking.

Rhythm of life *A group of musicians (above) in a fresco from the beginning of Egypt's New Kingdom (c1500 BC).*

From lumps of clay to works of art

Known as ceramics by archaeologists, pottery does not seem to have originated in any one particular culture. Instead, it appears to have been invented independently at various places. Starting from a few initial sites, it then spread throughout the world.

Test of time
From the Neolithic onwards, potters came up with practical, functional designs for their wares – shapes that have endured to the present day. These flasks with flanged necks date from around 4,000 years ago.

The first objects fashioned in fired clay by humans had no practical function: ancient figurines and beads from around 24,000 BC, found in what is now the Czech Republic, predate the first true pottery by at least 10,000 years and suggest that terracotta was used first to make ritual objects. What we term 'pottery' generally covers the battery of everyday utensils and receptacles that people use to store, carry or cook food. Examples of early functional pottery were originally believed to be associated with a settled way of life and a diet based around vegetables, soups and gruels made from cooked cereals.

The origins of pottery

For a long time, archaeologists thought that pottery originated in Mesopotamia and the surrounding area in *c*7000 BC, and that it followed hard on the heels of agriculture and animal husbandry. It turns out that other cultures do not fit neatly into this schema: pottery existed in Japan, for example, before the advent of agriculture, in the Jomon proto-civilisation that flourished from around 12,000 BC. Jomon fishermen and gatherers began to adopt a settled lifestyle in small communities from around 10,000 BC, and were primarily vegetarian. It is likely that the first receptacles were made for storing collected wild food, although pottery containers did not instantly supplant traditional woven baskets. Jomon pottery, of which many examples have survived, is decorated with patterns made by pressing a cord into the clay before firing. Indeed, the culture takes its name from this, as Jomon means 'cord marks'. While Jomon pottery has been found throughout Japan, the centre of Jomon culture is thought to have been the southern island of Kyushu.

At the same time, Neolithic peoples of the Sahara also discovered how to make pottery. The many remnants found indicate that early Saharan pottery was used across a wide area by nomads who subsisted by gathering wild cereals. Likewise, the emergence of pottery in the Caribbean and along the northern coast of South America (albeit later, *c*3000 BC) is also associated with hunter-gatherers rather than settled farmers. In the

Malleable material
The mouldable nature of raw clay was immediately exploited by sculptors. This ceramic figure (right) was made in Japan around the end of the 1st millennium BC.

Near East, by contrast, it is certain that pottery only made its first appearance with the development of agriculture.

Pottery took two quite distinct paths as it spread throughout Europe. The first began in Anatolia and followed the course of the River Danube, ultimately giving rise to what is known as Linear Band pottery, characterised by high-quality firing and painted designs of swags and simple objects. The second route saw pottery travel from the Levant (in the eastern Mediterranean, around Byblos) across the sea to the south of France and Spain. This line of development is referred to as Cardium Pottery or Impressed Ware, from the shells of a mollusc *Cardium edulis* that were used to press designs into the clay while it was still soft. By the beginning of the 6th millennium BC it had been taken by seafarers as far as southern France and Spain, and also flourished on the islands of Corsica and Sardinia. From the Danube, Linear Band-ware extended down the rivers Rhine, Elbe, Oder and Vistula, reaching as far as the Paris Basin almost 700 years later.

A universal material

Irrespective of origin, all pottery begins with the same raw material – clay. Made malleable by mixing with water, clay is easy to model

An ancient technique
Down the ages, the techniques used to make pottery have scarcely changed. Pots crafted and fired by African peoples today (below) bear a close resemblance to Danubian Neolithic pottery (left).

and shape. It is then hardened either by leaving it to dry in the sun or firing it in a kiln. The mineral composition of clay varies considerably according to the geology of its place of origin; it may, for instance, be more or less rich in limestone, or in metal oxides. In creating objects fit for particular purposes, the potter's first task is to choose the right type of clay for the job. Cooking utensils, for example, must use a non-limestone clay for their base material, as this has better heat-resistant properties. The addition of a tempering agent is also essential: depending on the materials to hand and the type of object being made, the tempering agent might be either fine sand, so-called 'grog' (finely ground fired clay), crushed bones or straw. Added to the clay mix, a tempering agent gives unfired clay an open-bodied texture, and these micropores allow any residual water to escape during the firing.

Once the clay mix has been prepared, water is added and the clay body left to rest – sometimes for several weeks – before being moulded by hand and modelled.

The modelling techniques of the first potters were fairly rudimentary: to make a hollow shape, for instance, the potter would press either his fist or a pestle into the clay, or shape the clay around a convex support.

Ongoing improvements

The quest to make pots more durable led early potters to devise new methods of construction. Building up pots from thin slabs of clay, stuck together with water, greatly increased their resistance to breakage. Moulding a pot from a single piece of clay – a more tricky technique – enabled the potter to make objects (notably bowls) of a regular thickness or to create relief decorations on the outer surface. Handles were added to make vases easier to carry, or sometimes small holes which could be hooked onto a finger, or threaded with a cord. The rather complex construction method known as

Vehicles for artistic expression
A red glazed ancient Egyptian vase from around 4000 BC is decorated with the incised outlines of ibex and antelope (left). A votive plaque from Corinth, dating from the 6th century BC (below) depicts a potter in front of his kiln.

'coiling' involved kneading pieces of clay into long sausage-like shapes, which were then coiled round to build up the sides of a pot; the outer surface was levelled by smoothing it over with water, which also ensured that the object would stay watertight. Later, potters invented the wheel, which opened the way for mass-production (see page 80).

From hot stones to kilns

It was probably by accident that people discovered that baking pottery, or at least drying it in the sun, gave it greater durability, and it is highly likely that clay objects were fired long before the invention of the kiln. The earliest pottery was baked on hot stones, or in front of large open fires. Later, to make earthenware pots even harder, they were fired in a pit covered with branches, straw and earth. This method lengthened the firing time, which could take several days. The invention of the kiln marked a decisive turning-point in the history of pottery: a kiln retains heat far more efficiently, distributes it more evenly and, above all, it reaches far higher temperatures. On the firing racks, where the temperature can exceed 1000°C, the metal

CHINESE PORCELAIN

In the 15th century BC, the Shang Dynasty invented a new form of pottery: celadon. Pots were fired at high temperatures after being coated with plant ash and feldspar. The colour of the finished pieces ranged from yellow to a bluish green. Under the Han Dynasty (206 BC–AD 222), many kilns were built in what is now Zhejiang province, which became China's main manufacturing centre for fine ceramic wares. Potters there pioneered methods of coating bisque (unglazed) ware with enamels and using metallic oxides to obtain vibrant colours. In the 3rd century AD, they succeeded in firing china clay to make pure white porcelain.

Ceremonial pottery
This intricate vase from the Bronze Age (above) indicates the high level of skill of potters working in the period, from around 3000 BC.

GLAZES – MAKING POTTERY MORE REFINED

From around 4000 BC, Egyptian potters, along with Chaldeans, Persians and Assyrians, began to produce a range of pots with different finishes – matt, lustred and with coloured glazes. The degree of glazing depended upon how much silica (silicon dioxide) there was in the clay itself; at very high firing temperatures the mineral took on a glassy appearance. In around 3000 BC, the Egyptians invented a glaze based on glassware that had been tinted through the addition of metal oxides (copper and iron), lead, caustic soda or lime. The resulting glaze colour ranged from vivid yellow to colourless.

oxides contained within the clay begin to melt; this is how the processes of vitrification and glazing came about.

The importance of decoration

Since its inception all pottery, even the simplest forms, has been decorated. Neolithic potters embellished their wares with striations and geometric motifs; sometimes, a potter would press a thumb into the damp clay to 'sign' the work. The ancient Egyptians had a taste for more elaborate decoration and they practised the art of 'engobing', in which artefacts were dipped into a bath containing water and finely powdered clay, and rubbed all over with this slip coating before firing. This made the surface of the pottery as smooth as a pebble.

Decorative features varied hugely from one era to another and between different regions. They have proved very fertile ground for archaeology, which has deciphered a whole typology of ornament on pottery: incised (made with a metal point, a knife, or stick), impressed (made by pressing some form of stamp, such as a seal, or a cord, into clay), moulded and painted.

All the colours of the rainbow

The appearance of clay is radically changed by firing, and this characteristic has been exploited for decorative purposes since Neolithic times. The final colour of a pot is determined by both the original colour of the clay and the temperature at which it is fired. Clays with negligible limestone content range from red to brown or even black. Limestone-rich clays tend to lighten during firing and come out orange, yellow or pale green. By the same token, natural mineral oxides in the clay affect the final colour. The Egyptians added red ochre or white ochre to their engobes, according to whether they wanted to enhance or tone down the natural colour of the clay base, and to ensure a uniform colour on the finished object.

From hand-weaving to the mechanised loom

More than 8,000 years ago, the invention in the Middle East of the hand loom – a simple wooden frame for tautening thread – opened the way for the varied and complex art of weaving. Gradually from this time, humans relinquished animal hides and pelts in favour of woven textiles for their clothes. The advent of the hand loom came at around the same time as people were abandoning a hunter-gatherer lifestyle for agriculture and livestock-rearing.

Women's work
Requiring both dexterity and patience, weaving became the preserve of women. This Maya sculpture from the 7th or 8th century AD (below) shows a woman using a backstrap loom. Traditional weaving skills are still kept alive by women in many parts of the world, such as India (right) and Guatemala (far right).

Neolithic farming people in the Near East had mastered the art of basket-weaving, becoming expert in the skill of plaiting nets, baskets and mats. It was a short step from intertwining bulrush stems to doing the same with finer threads to produce fabrics. Yet it soon became clear that some kind of apparatus was needed to hold the threads taut. The hand-loom was the result, initially very rough and ready, but later increasingly sophisticated. The oldest known fragments of woven cloth – one of which comes from Anatolia, *c*6000 BC, and the other, *c*5000 BC, from the Fayum Oasis in Egypt – show great regularity in the weave.

A cottage industry

Women wove linen and also wool, camelhair and goat hair. The first step was to prepare the fibres. With linen, this meant separating the flax (the raw plant fibre from which linen is made) by stripping away the woody parts of the plant stems. Wool fibres had to be washed and carded (untangled) by running the fingers through them. In the Near East, the spindle and distaff were invented as a way of creating long yarns. The Neolithic spindle is a simple wooden stick mounted on a disc made of stone or clay – the whorl – which allows the spindle to keep rotating steadily, like a top. Spinners draw out unspun threads that have been wrapped loosely around the distaff, twists them between the fingers and fastens them onto a hook or slit cut in the end of the spindle. They then twirl the spindle – the motion is maintained by the whorl – which acts as a flywheel. As the spindle rotates, it twists and stretches the woollen threads into yarn. The more tightly wound the threads, the stronger they become. The end result is flexible yarn of a regular thickness. Textiles woven from different yarns vary in weight and are suitable for different climates or seasons. After being dyed, patterned, cut and sewn, fabrics lend themselves to an infinite variety of forms. Thus arose the whole art of making clothes and of dressing to impress.

Shuttles, heddles and sheds

To begin with, the loom was nothing more than a simple frame on which weavers would stretch the yarns, one by one, keeping them straight and parallel to form the warp of a fabric. There are many ancient depictions of this activity: one is on a 6,400-year-old piece of pottery found at Badari in Egypt.

The weaver would then interlace the weft thread by hand, alternately passing it over one warp thread and under the next. Before long, weavers began using a stick with yarn wound

rods separated the odd and even warp threads, so allowing the shuttle to pass swiftly through the gap (the 'shed') between them without having to weave laboriously around each thread one by one. The position of the heddle was switched around for the shuttle's return pass.

A shared innovation

From the 4th millennium BC, cotton was cultivated in India, from where it spread to the Near East, Africa and Europe. Wild cotton was also woven in Mexico and later Peru. Meanwhile, in China silk thread was the impetus behind advances in loom technology from the 3rd millennium BC. The Chinese

Patterned weave
The intricately woven fabrics worn by the figures on this Egyptian funerary mural (left) show how far weaving had progressed by the 15th century BC.

around it as a 'shuttle'. On larger horizontal or on vertical looms, the warp threads would be weighted down with stones to give the required tension. The first real technological refinement of the loom came with the addition of two horizontal rods, known as heddles: all the even warp threads were attached to one heddle and all the odd warp threads to the other. Simply pulling on one or other of the

BASKETRY – FORERUNNER OF WEAVING

The oldest known fragments of basketry are some 8,000-year-old remnants found in the desert sands of Egypt and in a cave at Los Murcielagos in Spain. These Neolithic scraps show that basket-weaving techniques were firmly established and well developed by this time. Alongside traditional methods of weaving, some basketry also indicates that a technique known as sparterie weaving, using the grass *Machrochloa tenacissima*, primarily

for making grain baskets, was already being practised. In this technique, the basketmaker creates a kind of sausage of straw or other material, which is secured and bound tightly using strips of linden bark or willow canes, threading these around the straw with a large needle. Rush mats were used in Egypt and Mesopotamia to wrap and carry goods. They also served as carpets and wall hangings, and even as screens and roofing materials.

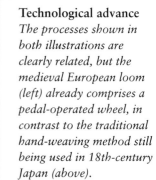

Technological advance
The processes shown in both illustrations are clearly related, but the medieval European loom (left) already comprises a pedal-operated wheel, in contrast to the traditional hand-weaving method still being used in 18th-century Japan (above).

COLOURING CLOTH

Textile dyes developed alongside weaving, from the Neolithic onwards. They came to command high prices and play a major role in the economies of the Near and Middle East, due to their rarity and the know-how involved in their manufacture. Dyes were at the root of the prosperity and fame of certain regions, such as the Indus Valley, where madder was produced from around 3000 BC, or the coast of Syria, from around 1500 BC, thanks to the Tyrian purple dye which was made from the *Murex* sea snail common there.

Dyes were extracted from the leaves, roots, seeds and husks of plants, as well as from insects and seashells. Crimson, for instance, came from two insects – the Cochineal bug and the Polish kermes; blue was produced by indigo dyes made from plants; yellows and oranges came from saffron. Some blue dyes (such as orchil) can be obtained by steeping lichens in an ammoniac solution such as urine. Recipes for dyes were devised by trial and error and handed down secretly. The first to be written down, in the 8th century BC, are only sketchy.

In the basic dyeing technique, the yarn or fabric is first cleaned so it is grease-free. Some fibres, such as wool, are treated with a 'mordant' such as alum or metallic salts. Mordanting – the process of fixing the colour – is achieved by immersing the yarn or fabric into a hot dye bath.

Natural dyes were not supplanted until the 19th century, and even then many remained in use. The world's first synthetic aniline dye was mauveine purple, discovered by the English chemist William Henry Perkin in 1856.

invented a pedal loom in around 2000 BC to solve the problem of how to reel in and unwind the warp threads during weaving. By pressing down with the feet on a wooden bar, weavers could move the unwound threads at the top of the loom, while the woven fabric gathered at the bottom.

Silk weaving did not become established in the West until the Middle Ages. Up until then, the loom in Europe saw only minor changes in design. The invention of the spinning wheel in 13th-century Germany represented the first step towards mechanisation. Key technological innovations emerged in 18th-century Britain: John Kay's flying shuttle (1733), James Hargreaves' 'Spinning Jenny' (1764) and Richard Arkwright's water frame (1769) – improvements in machines for spinning and weaving came thick and fast. The automation programme proposed in 18th-century France by inventor Jacques de Vaucanson became a reality with the invention of the Jacquard loom in 1808. The Industrial Revolution was underway.

Chewing gum c4500 BC

Remarkably, Neolithic people were already using chewing gum some 6,500 years ago. In 1997, archaeologists working in Sweden discovered a piece of prehistoric chewing gum made from birch-bark extract, with teeth marks still in it. We also know that the Egyptians of the pharaonic period used resin from the mastic tree to make a kind of chewing gum. The bark tar that formed the base of these early gums is believed to have had antiseptic properties.

A Papuan woman *blows a bubble with the gum she is chewing.*

AN AMERICAN SYMBOL

The first chewing gums based on chicle – a resin from a tree that grew originally on the Yucatán peninsula of Mexico – appeared in the USA in the 19th century. In 1869, a patent was issued to the American photographer Thomas Adams for chewing gum made from a compound of natural rubber and various flavourings. It was a hit with the public and, from 1900 onwards, it began to be mass-produced.

Drums c4000 BC

Prehistoric peoples noticed that a hollowed-out tree trunk, or a skin stretched across any empty vessel, made a wonderfully resonant sound when struck with the hands or a stick. The sound is produced by the mass of air within the object vibrating. The first indications that the discovery can be traced back to Neolithic times came from wall paintings and pottery in Eastern Europe. The evidence is all the more compelling since we know that by the end of the Neolithic people had mastered the technique of lacing, which would have been a pre-requisite for stretching a skin over a drumhead. This is an important feature: the true drum, and all the instruments that descend from it, is characterised by the fact that the drumhead can be tightened or slackened, either to prolong the resonance or to raise the pitch.

The playing of drums is reliably attested in Egypt during the 4th millennium BC. Cylinders made of terracotta or bronze covered at both ends with scraps of skin were used as instruments in military music. Introduced to the south of the country by the Nubians, they would be played by armies on the march. Among the Romans and Greeks, wood tended to be used for the body of the drum; these instruments resembled the timbrel (a form of tambourine) that was already in use among the Israelites. In China, drums were often made of metal. Although drums come in various shapes and sizes, can be covered at just one or at both ends, and are played in various positions – on the ground, held between the feet or under the armpit, or slung across the chest – the basic principle of the drum has always remained the same.

Rhythm section
Drums come in many shapes and sizes, and are played all round the world. The instrument was popular in 1st-century BC Mexico (above left) and has been used for centuries by many African peoples, such as these drummers from Burundi (above).

Kohl *c*3750 BC

The ancient Egyptians set great store by personal hygiene and were fastidious about appearance. It is no surprise, therefore, that they were fond of perfumes or unguents, the forerunners of cosmetics. From the first half of the 4th millennium BC, both women and men would line their eyes with a dark powder called kohl, a habit that has survived to the present day and spread worldwide.

Medicinal properties

Like many cosmetics, kohl was originally used for medicinal purposes. The effect of this compound, which is based on antimony (Arabic: *kuhl*) is to stimulate the tear ducts. Tears helped to keep the eyes lubricated and so prevented infections, which was important in desert regions where dust or insects were easily blown into the eyes. Antimony also acts as an antiseptic. Egyptians of the Old Kingdom (*c*2720–2160 BC) knew about these properties; they were already using copper vessels lined with antimony to carry water.

Eye of the falcon

The ancient Egyptians, who also used the lead compound galena for making kohl, clearly regarded it as a beauty product, using it to draw attention to the eyes. Yet it also had a symbolic role: a person's eyes outlined in black recalled Horus, the falcon-headed deity, whose all-seeing eyes represented the sun and moon.

Highly prized pot
Kohl has long been prized in North Africa as a cosmetic and antiseptic; this ceramic kohl pot comes from 15th-century BC Egypt. Kohl is still used by many people today, including the Tuareg nomads of Niger (top).

EASTERN ALLURE

In the ancient world, kohl was by no means restricted to Egypt: the Bible, for example, mentions that it was used by Jezebel, the pagan queen of Israel (c900 BC). Jezebel hailed from Phoenicia, whose seafaring merchants traded goods from states all around the Mediterranean, including Egypt.

Kohl remained popular among women in the Middle East throughout the rise and spread of Islam from the early 7th century AD. Even nowadays, in Muslim countries from the Maghreb in North Africa to the eastern Mediterranean, women still line their eyes and those of their children with kohl to ward off evil spirits. They occasionally even smear it on the navels of newborn babies after the umbilical cord has been cut in order to prevent infection. Nor were Western women to be outshone: although for a long time they paid more attention to their complexion and lips, with the introduction of mascara in the early 20th century they discovered the allure of the Oriental look.

Perfume c3500 BC

Some 5,500 years ago, in the temples of Thebes (Luxor), priests worshipped the gods of eternal Egypt by burning sweet-smelling incense. This was the form in which perfume (from Latin *per fumum*, literally 'through smoke') first appeared. Preparations for these fumigation rituals followed a strict liturgical protocol involving dozens of ingredients. Grapes, honey, myrrh, and cardamon – to name just a few – were placed in censers where burning coals released their vapours. This was the simplest method of producing a perfume, but the Egyptians were quick to adopt another, more sophisticated method. They noticed that fat tended to retain smells. Steeping the petals of perfumed flowers, spices or resins in fat allowed them to create perfumed oils and unguents, which doctors used to cure patients. The ancient Egyptians believed that illnesses were the result of demons that entered the body through wounds. Applied to the skin, scented oils would give off vapours to drive evil spirits away. Yet oils and unguents were not confined to the sick and the gods. From around 3500 BC, women began to deploy scents as part of their daily toilet – and in particular as an aid to seduction. Queens of Egypt right up to Cleopatra VII used perfumes as a way of enhancing their sex appeal.

Precious liquid
Perfumes were a costly luxury. Roman women of the 1st century AD kept them in exquisite vials.

An elegant censer
This bronze thurible, or incense burner, in the shape of a hawk (below), dates from the end of the 12th century AD. It reflects the high level of craftsmanship in Islamic art.

FASHION STATEMENT

The Greeks and Romans expanded both the range and use of scents. In the early Olympic Games, athletes would rub themselves with perfumed oils. In the 1st century BC, the Romans invented the perfume bottle made of blown glass. Meanwhile, in the 1st century AD, Pliny the Elder wrote the first scientific treatise on the manufacture and classification of perfumes in his *Natural History*. Later, the Arabs invented the alembic (an alchemical still) and the distilling process: employing heat, water and plant extracts, distillation yielded a concentrated perfume extract – an essential oil. As connoisseurs of spices, the Arabs also enhanced the range of scents. Crusaders returning from the Holy Land in the 11th and 12th centuries introduced these skills to Europe. This helped to revive the use of perfumes to disguise body odours in an age when washing and bathing were less frequent than today.

73

THE POTTER'S WHEEL – c3500 BC
A craftsman's tool

The invention of the potter's wheel provided great impetus to the development of ceramics, facilitating larger-scale production and a wider range of objects. The earliest known wheel-made pottery is the smooth 'red ware' found at Erech and Tell el-Obeid in Mesopotamia (c3500 BC).

Pottery first appeared at the very outset of the Neolithic, in around 7000 BC. By 5000 BC, pottery-making was a major activity in several parts of the ancient world, including what would become Egypt. Yet the tools available to early potters had changed little: all they had were their hands and the clay, which was manipulated in strips, moulded and built up into the finished article ready for drying. As they worked, potters smoothed the surface of the wet clay with a moist pad. Occasionally, they would use a pestle or some other convex-shaped object to help fashion a hollow receptacle.

The turntable – a rudimentary wheel

Historians are not certain when wheels first became part of mechanical devices, but it is widely believed that the potter's wheel may have existed before the first wheeled vehicles. There is evidence from Ur in Mesopotamia and from Iran that potters in the late 4th millennium BC were making their wares on a rudimentary disc of wood or clay. This enabled the potter to turn the lump of clay while keeping his hands steady, rather than having to move around the object. The result was smoother, more evenly shaped pots.

Later, the disc was fixed to a vertical axis, creating a genuine turntable (a 'tournette'). Even so, the device was unwieldy and required considerable effort to turn it. The potter, sitting on the ground, had to keep shoving the turntable, which would spin for a few revolutions under its own momentum before needing another shove. Some would have an apprentice to spin the wheel for them. Once the wheel reached a high enough speed – around 100 rpm – centrifugal force kicked in, giving further impetus to the rotary motion. At this speed, the potter was able to pull up the clay into the desired shape, be it vase, cup or jar. It is likely that the fast-spinning wheel was discovered by chance, when a sufficiently heavy wheel was fixed to an axis and, once set in motion, kept spinning of its own accord.

Stick-driven wheels

Fast hand-driven potter's wheels spread throughout the Mediterranean region: the Egyptians were using them from 2750 BC,

Tools of the trade *Potters in the Moluccas in Indonesia use a range of basic tools (top right): a split piece of bamboo to turn the neck of a pot, a forked spatula to decorate it, and knives to trim the edges. Tools almost identical to these were used 3,600 years ago by Minoan craftsmen on Crete to make exquisite pottery (above).*

CENTRIFUGAL FORCE

Discovered through empirical observation, the phenomenon known as centrifugal force, by which an object is pushed towards the edge of a rotating body, remained unexplained for centuries. In demonstrating that mechanics are based on the relationship between force and acceleration, the scientists Galileo Galilei (1564–1642) and most notably Isaac Newton (1643–1727) established the laws of dynamics. In around 1920, the chemist and Nobel laureate Theodor Svedberg devised the ultracentrifuge, the first examples of which rotated at 1,000 rpm, but which later reached astonishing speeds of 1000 revolutions per second. One modern application of centrifugal force is to separate out blood into its constituent cells and fluid.

THE FOOT-DRIVEN POTTER'S WHEEL

The prime concern behind all technical improvements to the potter's wheel was how to free the potter's hands so that full attention could be given to the piece being made. Medieval inventors came up with a device comprising two wheels linked by a long axle.

By kicking the lower wheel, the potter set in motion the upper wheel – the 'batterboard,' where the pots are 'thrown'. The true foot-driven potter's wheel, characterised by a heavy, large-diameter inertia flywheel to rotate the batterboard, did not appear until the 15th century AD.

Pottery then and now
The potter's workshop depicted above is set in early 19th-century England. The photograph shows a contemporary Indian potter at work in the open air, pulling up the sides of a pot on his treadle-driven wheel.

while many remains confirm their presence on Crete from around 2000 BC. Yet they still had the disadvantage that a lone potter needed one hand free almost continuously in order to keep the wheel spinning. A major improvement came with the addition of a stick that every so often engaged with notches cut into the perimeter of the wheel and kept it rotating at the required rate; wheels that could be spun continuously like this were introduced in Mesopotamia in around 700 BC. In widespread use during the Roman period, the stick-driven wheel persisted throughout the Middle Ages in Europe.

Yet the true potter's wheel is the foot-driven version: powered by depressing a treadle linked to a crankshaft, it leaves both hands completely free. Some wall-paintings from Mesopotamia and Egypt, showing potters seated in front of wheels with their feet pressing down on a bar, appeared to suggest that this technology was around as early as the 4th millennium BC. Closer inspection has shown these devices to be merely variants of the stick-driven wheel.

THE WHEEL – c3500 BC
The world's most far-reaching invention

The wheel represented a giant leap forward for humankind. Few other inventions have gone on to so radically transform people's lives. It revolutionised transport, opening up communications, trade and the exchange of ideas between cultures. It also gave rise to other mechanical innovations such as the gearwheel, cog, pulley and gyroscope.

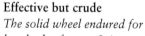

Effective but crude
The solid wheel endured for hundreds of years. It is shown here on two vehicles from the 1st millennium BC. The four-wheeled chariot above is a votive offering from Ugarit on the east Mediterranean coast, while the two-wheeled royal chariot (left) is from Sumer.

The common denominator between such diverse inventions as the potter's wheel, spinning wheel, chariot, windmill and bicycle is, of course, the wheel. Without the wheel none of these wonderful devices would have seen the light of day. But when did it first appear?

While felling trees for building, Neolithic people would have found that a round log that rolled saved a great deal of effort. From this must have come the realisation that heavy loads could be moved more easily by placing logs underneath as rollers. Over time, a more efficient solution – a wheel that rotated on a fixed axle – replaced the rollers, which had constantly to be repositioned. In addition, given its small circumference, it takes less energy to turn an axle than a whole wheel. No wooden vehicular wheels have survived from ancient times to help us date the development, but there are surviving clay potter's wheels, which historians think were invented at around the same time, from the mid-4th millennium BC.

Different civilisations came up with the wheel independently. It was unknown in Old Kingdom Egypt; the builders of the pyramids devised a system of sleds and ramps to manoeuvre the massive stone blocks into position. Much later, the Incas of Peru erected the impressive stone structures typical of their empire without the aid of the wheel. The oldest axle wheels to be identified come from the Sumerian, Akkadian, Elamite and Chaldean cultures of Mesopotamia. In China, the wheel first appeared around 2800 BC.

The first chariots

The earliest evidence of a vehicle with axled wheels is a pictogram engraved *c*3200 BC on a tablet in the temple of Inanna at Erech in Mesopotamia, showing a chariot with two solid wheels. The wheels do not appear to have been cut from a single piece of wood, but rather to comprise two or three pieces bracketed together and sawn into a circular shape. The axles went through the centre of each wheel and were held in place by lynchpins. There was room for improvement: the overall arrangement was fragile and, because the axles were integral to the chassis, the whole vehicle would have to be lifted and turned to change direction. Even so, this crude chariot represented a major advance, making it possible for people to travel long distances on something other than the back of a beast of burden, and to transport loads by harnessing the motive power of animals.

Transportation and warfare

The earliest wheeled vehicles were probably based on the travois – a type of sled made by lashing two long poles together to form a frame in the shape of an isoceles triangle. The base of the triangle dragged along the ground, while its apex was harnessed to the person or animal pulling it. On top of the frame was a platform or netting to carry the load. All that was required to create a chariot was to mount the lower end of the travois onto an axle with two wheels and place a box-like body on top. Mounted on either two or four solid wheels, early chariots were heavy contraptions drawn by teams of oxen or mules.

A variant of this basic design, comprising a body with a high front to protect the occupants from arrows, entered service with the Sumerians as a war chariot in around 2500 BC. It was used as a mobile shooting platform on the battlefield, but was too unwieldy for launching swift attacks.

The spoked wheel and the horse

The most significant advance in the history of transport came in Mesopotamia at the start of the 2nd millennium BC – the spoked wheel. Far less heavy than solid wheels in either wood or bronze, the spoked wheel enabled the development of lighter and faster two-wheeled chariots with semi-circular bodies.

As so often in the history of technology, the development did not occur in isolation. The horse had been introduced into the region in the 18th century BC, when Hittite forces invaded and overthrew the Amorite dynasty, and quickly spread throughout Mesopotamia. Fast and resilient, yet easy to train and maintain, horses were ideally suited to pulling the new light chariots. They were used initially in warfare, and later adapted to carry people and goods. Even by this stage, the ability to travel easily from place to place had transformed people's lives and greatly facilitated communications,

Chariot of the sun
A well-known Bronze Age artefact from Trundholm in Denmark (left) shows that the spoked wheel was in use by 1500 BC.

Built for speed
An Assyrian relief of c668–630 BC shows a soldier guarding the light, fast hunting chariot of King Ashurbanipal.

Wheel evolution
From the solid wheel (left) to the chariot wheel, handcart wheel and bicycle wheel, technology has been constantly evolving in the search for lightness and comfort of ride.

a vital factor within extensive empires. The need for good communications to speed their legions around their empire drove the Romans to develop the first proper road network, which already covered 80,000 kilometres (50,000 miles) by the start of the 3rd century AD.

Perfecting the wheel

It was during the time of the Roman Empire that the Celts made an important discovery: a hot-forged metal wheel rim, made in a single piece and bound to the wheel with strips of iron, produced a far more durable wheel than any previous arrangement. The improvement went hand in hand with the introduction of wooden or bronze sleeves (or even hardwood bearings) between the wheel hub and the axle to reduce friction at this critical point, so ensuring that all the component parts lasted much longer. The wheel continued to evolve, undergoing numerous modifications for use on a wide range of animal or human-powered vehicles, such as the handcart, the horse-drawn carriage and the stagecoach, before being used on the world's first mechanised mode of transport: the bicycle.

In the late 19th century, bicycle wheels were given a rubber rim – the tyre, which greatly improved the comfort of the ride. Along with the internal combustion engine, this innovation ultimately gave rise to the motor car. In more recent times, the wheel has undergone further improvements, such as rims made of light alloys and composite materials such as carbon fibre.

Increased energy

Transport was far from being the only application of the wheel. From as early as the 3rd millennium BC, millstones were being used to grind cereals and to produce wine and oil. Driven either by hand or by animal power, these ancient devices spread to Egypt in the 4th century BC and reached western Europe three centuries later.

In the 2nd millennium BC, an invention appeared almost simultaneously in the Near East and in some parts of Asia and Africa: this was the noria – the first of several machines devised for lifting water. Moved by muscle power, the noria consists of a large undershot waterwheel, with paddles on its rim and scoops mounted all around its circumference. Sited on the bank of a river or pond, it draws up water, then deposits it into a system of channels that irrigate the surrounding fields. The noria, which is still a familiar sight in certain parts of the Near East and Africa, may well be the ancestor of the watermill, which first appeared at the end of the 1st millennium BC in the Roman Empire.

Revolutionary technologies

The wheel has been the driving force behind several important technological innovations. One such was the cogwheel, which the Chinese probably knew from the 3rd millennium BC, and which first appeared in ancient Greece in around 400 BC. Having fallen into disuse, it was 'rediscovered' by Archimedes of Syracuse (287–212 BC), who has gone down in history as the

inventor of gearing. The watermill powered by a horizontal paddle wheel, which was widely used by the Greeks, was supplanted by the vertical mill – the first to use a system of gearwheels to transmit the motion of the wheel to a horizontal shaft driving the millstone. The Roman engineer Vitruvius (c80–c15 BC) described this mechanism in 25 BC, defining the apparatus as a composite tool 'working artificially through combinations of wheels'. Thereafter, engineers became adept at using gearing systems to transmit or increase motive power. One especially popular form of gearing, which remained in widespread use right up to the 18th century, were cage (or lantern) gears, whose teeth are comprised of little cylindrical

Animal power
A horizontally mounted wheel, powered by a bullock, drives an Archimedes' screw that draws water up from a well to fill irrigation channels. This technology is some 2,000 years old but is still in use today.

Universal symbol
From the cogwheel –
which Charlie Chaplin
(in his 1936 film Modern
Times*) made into a*
universal emblem of the
dehumanised industrial
world – to the large Ferris
Wheels at fairgrounds,
the wheel has become a
powerful symbol of motion,
action and progress.

wooden rods, parallel to the axle and arranged in a circle around it. If gearing had never been invented, then paddle wheels and windmills (both of which prefigured screw propulsion), clocks and bicycle chains would never have seen the light of day.

Dawn of the machine age

Another variant of the cogwheel, the pulley, is first mentioned in the *Mechanica*, a work from the school of Aristotle in the 4th century BC. Combined with the winch, the pulley stimulated the development of new kinds of press, which came into their own with the invention of the screw. The winch and pulley were also used to construct the first cranes. Archimedes is credited with having invented the

triple-pulley crane, which greatly increased the tension that could be exerted on a rope with just a winch. These inventions made it possible for heavier loads to be lifted, paving the way both for the architectural achievements of the Greeks and Romans and, later, the Gothic cathedrals of Europe.

Modern applications

In around 1800, an Englishman named George Cayley drew up designs for a tension-spoked wheel that he planned to incorporate into a flying machine he was building. In the event, the first actual application of this light yet strong form of wheel was on the bicycle. In 1870, the British engineer James Starley manufactured a wheel whose wire spokes could be re-tightened whenever they worked loose. His solution was to run the spokes off the hub at a tangent, and this configuration enabled them to withstand better the stresses of acceleration and braking.

From the 1910s onwards, the gyroscope began to play a vital role in navigational systems for ships and aircraft. When the flywheel of the gyroscope is set in motion, it stabilises in a particular plane. As long as it keeps spinning, it will always maintain the same orientation in space. In 1912, the first automatic pilot was built using the gyrocompass.

FROM THE SPINDLE TO THE SPINNING WHEEL

The spinning wheel, which was invented in China or India between 500 and 1000 AD, first appeared in the West in the 8th or 9th century during the time of the Moors in Spain. Prior to this, people used a large wheel that was little more than an outsized version of the spindle; the unwieldy device was operated by hand, with the spinner alternately rotating the wheel and then winding the twisted thread onto the bobbin. By contrast, the spinning wheel had a pedal, which left the spinner's hands free to unravel the yarn, as well as twisting and reeling it onto the bobbin. This all made for much faster work, and widespread use of this technology saw the growth of a textile industry in the Middle Ages.

Ultra-light wheels
In competitive cycling
and motorsport, the
wheel has been
improved to meet
the demand for ever
higher performance.

The saw c3500 BC

The origins of the saw almost certainly lie in the finely serrated flints made by prehistoric man. The first saws we know of made of metal (c3500 BC) were fashioned in copper and later in bronze. By around 1200 BC, thanks to the use of iron, saws were being made that could cut tree trunks into planks, while from the mid-7th century BC, iron saws were even capable of cutting stone, as indicated by the clear saw marks found on stone blocks from the pyramids of Egypt.

Welding

c3500 BC

From the 4th millennium BC, the Mesopotamians used welding to join together thin sheets of gold. One invaluable characteristic of this precious metal is that, once heated, it can easily be welded to itself without leaving any marks. Autogeneous welding, as this process is known, developed on a large scale from around 1500 BC, as the Hittites began mining iron-ore deposits. Yet blacksmiths tried in vain to do the same with copper and bronze.

It was doubtless through a process of trial and error, heating metals that were readily to hand, that someone hit upon the technique of using a connecting metal – namely tin – to form a bond; this process is called heterogeneous welding. Right up to the 19th century, the only form of welding was forge welding, and it was not until the early years of the 20th century, and the invention of arc welding, that it became a common assembly method in industry.

Longlasting bond *The various segments of sheet gold in this Sumerian necklace were welded together almost 5,000 years ago.*

No change *The design of the bow saw (above) has barely altered. Modern tools look much like the one in this medieval illustration.*

MODERN WELDING

Ultrasonic welding is used to join different metals or bond metals to ceramics, such as in batteries for electric vehicles. Electron beam welding made it possible to assemble the titanium fuel tank for the European Ariane V space rocket. When welding in tight spaces is called for, robots have replaced human welders. All told, there are currently around 300 different welding techniques.

Fra Angelico's nails *The renowned Italian Renaissance artist painted the nails used at Christ's crucifixion.*

The nail

c3500 BC

Around 3500 BC, in Mesopotamia, sheets of metal could only be joined together, or fixed to wooden, stone or copper objects, either by using leather straps or small pegs made of wood or bone. Since neither method made a very strong bond, they were gradually supplanted by a new kind of peg made from hammered copper (later bronze) – in other words, the nail.

Mesopotamian nails came in various sizes and looked very much like nails we use today, but the metals they were made from were too soft to be truly effective. As a result, it was not until the advent of iron that nails caught on elsewhere.

The emergence of the written word

At the site of the Great Temple in the Sumerian city of Uruk (modern Warka in Iraq), clay tablets dating from 3200 BC have been found listing the number of sacks of grain and head of cattle owned by the temple. Such finds appear to confirm that writing owes its genesis not to literary ambition, but rather to the demands of bureaucracy.

It is easy to picture Sumerian scribes compiling inventories of commodities, which multiplied with the spread of settled agriculture and irrigation. As prosperity grew, generating ever larger surpluses, the spoken word and people's memories could no longer be trusted to keep track of stores and their distribution. Increasingly, administrators came to rely on aide-memoires, including notches on fragments of bone or stone, earthenware tokens or pictograms scratched on smooth pebbles.

Tallying and noting things down became all the more vital once people began to gather in communities numbering several thousand, such as at Uruk, the first city built on the banks of the Euphrates, which had important trade links with the interior of Mesopotamia.

Sacred writing

Before ascribing this momentous discovery entirely to bureaucratic innovation, it is worth noting that the written word may also have derived from another, less prosaic source. Divination – especially the branch known as haruspicy, which involved reading the entrails of animals – was a common practice in ancient Mesopotamia. Soothsayers, who were temple functionaries, collected messages imparted by the gods. In time, they may have begun to write those messages down, as soothsayers did in ancient China, another place where writing systems emerged from an early age.

The first known Chinese written characters are on so-called 'dragon bones' (in fact, bones of deer and cattle, or fragments of turtle shell) that date from the 13th century BC. These were used for divination in a process that involved heating the bones, then inspecting resulting cracks for answers to questions. The bones were then inscribed with the questions and answers.

Chinese tradition saw writing as a gift from the gods, and the same was true in Egypt, where writing appeared in the 4th millennium BC. The word 'hieroglyph' literally means 'sacred carving'. The ancient Egyptians believed that the written word was a gift bestowed on the human race by the ibis-headed god Thoth.

Powerful bookkeepers

It is significant that writing came into being in urban societies, which had rigid social and political hierarchies

Sacred and secular
The symbols on this Chinese 'dragon bone' of c1300 BC (above) record a divination process. In contrast, this cuneiform writing of c3200–3000 BC (right) is a commercial inventory.

Respectable position
Scribes occupied a position of honour and respect in ancient Egyptian society. When writing, the scribe would unroll the bottom of the papyrus scroll with his left hand, while rolling up the top with his right.

SCRIBES IN EGYPTIAN SOCIETY

A piece of advice recorded in about 1225 BC is revealing about the status of scribes in Egyptian society: 'If you want to avoid back-breaking and difficult work, become a scribe.' The scribe, a man of letters, was exempt from hard manual labour in the fields. He had to be temperamentally suited to spending his days bent over papyrus. As state officials, scribes recorded everything that occurred in the land of the Pharaohs and were vital cogs in the Egyptian administrative machine. The work was demanding, and the perks that scribes enjoyed, such as tax exemption, were earned only after a long apprenticeship in the 'Houses of Life', the archives attached to temples. There, scribes learned how to make ink, to prepare their writing brushes and to draw the 700 or so hieroglyphic symbols used in New Kingdom Egypt.

A terracotta tablet and its 'envelope'
Tablets of writing found in Cappadocia, southern Turkey (below right), represent an ingenious ancient form of the modern letter. They date from c2000–1800 BC.

and established religion. Cuneiform writing, involving lines or symbols in the form of little wedges (*cuneus* is Latin for 'wedge'), originated in the city of Uruk. From there it spread rapidly, first within the borders of Mesopotamia and then, from the end of the 3rd millennium BC, throughout the Near East. In Egypt, the first proto-hieroglyphs appeared from the 4th millennium onwards. Hieroglyphic writing really took off with the unification of Upper and Lower Egypt into one state in around 3100 BC.

In all instances, the written word developed and spread in response to the needs of a centralised administration. In ancient Mesopotamia, Egypt and China, an army of scribes or mandarins was trained to compile population censuses, land registers and inventories of yields from harvests.

Legislation and correspondence

Eager to tap into the wealth within their domains, rulers were quick to regulate commercial activity. Commercial contracts were issued granting people the right to trade in certain commodities.

Mesopotamia and Egypt maintained not only trade links with one another, but also

INSTANTLY ACCESSIBLE IMAGES

At the root of all writing systems are pictograms – stylised images that represent objects, living things and concepts (hence their alternative name of ideograms). For instance, sacks of grain appear on the earliest Mesopotamian documents alongside a hand, and these symbols are thought to signify a particular person's ownership of the commodity. Such images are almost instantly recognisable, but others – such as a stylised bull's head (denoting cattle) or a curve resting on a horizontal line with vertical lines beneath it (the symbol for the sky) – require a more thorough knowledge of Sumerian tablets to be deciphered. The gap between the character and the thing it signifies increases in cuneiform script, comprised of straight or angled shapes and lines, as it does in Chinese script. By contrast, Egyptian hieroglyphs spurned such conceptual advances, retaining images that appear more immediately accessible to the observer. In fact, the fine details in hieroglyphs are so rich in meaning that experts can tell precisely what species of bird or plant is denoted by a particular inscription on stone or painted symbol on a papyrus roll.

The transcription of sounds

Yet all these writing systems underwent a common evolution. Gradually, the systems grew more complex in order to give a true rendition of phrases as they were actually spoken; in other words, written languages began to take syntax, or grammar, into account. A crucial development was that the symbols, which hitherto stood for single objects or concepts, began to be used to transcribe spoken sounds. So a symbol could simultaneously designate a word and represent a sound. For example, the Sumerian pictogram for arrow denoted an arrow (called a 'ti'), but could mean 'life', a word that was also pronounced 'ti'. Similarly, the Egyptian hieroglyph for a hoe might refer to the familiar implement used by agricultural peasants, or to its homophone, the word for 'love', as both were pronounced 'mer'.

The coexistence of ideograms and phonetic symbols entailed, in turn, the use of determinative signs, which act as keys that tell the reader how a character should be interpreted.

diplomatic relations. Writing was key to the development of foreign policy and the drafting of treaties. For example, in the 14th century BC King Ashur-Uballit of Assyria lodged a complaint with the Egyptian Pharaoh Amenhotep III that he has not yet received the gold owing to him in return for his signature on a peace treaty between the two states. 'In your country, gold is like dust; you only have to bend down and pick it up. So why are you being so stingy with it?', complains the Assyrian ruler. The letter is inscribed on one of many terracotta tablets discovered at Amarna in Egypt in 1887, which contain the copious correspondence of the 18th-dynasty pharaohs, Amenhotep III and IV. The letters are composed in cuneiform writing, rather than Egyptian hieroglyphs, showing that official translators already existed at this stage, and that the cuneiform writing system had spread far beyond the borders of Sumer.

Reading matter
A detail from the ancient Egyptian 'Book of the Dead' (background, left), found in the tomb of Thutmose III in Thebes (left).

Taking dictation
A relief carving (right) conveys a powerful impression of scribes hanging on the pharaoh's every word.

Spreading the word

Cuneiform characters developed in Sumerian proved just as suitable for transcribing Akkadian, the language of the Semitic people who around 2300 BC became rulers over Mesopotamia. Cuneiform writing was also used in the kingdoms of Babylon, Assyria and Elam, then later in the Persian Empire, by the Hittites in Anatolia, in the kingdom of Urartu in Armenia and by the Canaanites in Palestine.

In China, writing played an important part in bringing cultural and political unity to the country as the Middle Kingdom. The Chinese script was later adopted, then altered, by the Koreans and Japanese. One advantage of the complex Oriental writing system was that the ideogram was far enough removed from what it stood for that the written characters transcribing one language could be adopted by people speaking another language or dialect.

Codifying laws and creating literature

The codification of religious and social laws is a major factor in societies becoming more enlightened. Hammurabi, the ruler of Babylon from 1793 to 1750 BC, was the first ruler known to collect the laws of his kingdom into a single code, which he had inscribed in stone still known as the Code of Hammurabi. In doing so, by his own account, he was seeking to 'shine on his people like the Sun and illuminate the whole land', with the aim of 'proclaiming the rule of law ... and eradicating all that is wicked and unjust, to prevent the strong from oppressing the weak'.

Since the advent of writing, humans have shown an inexhaustible urge to record the past, disseminate knowledge – and generate myths. Writing spawned both history and literature. It is surely no coincidence that 'The Epic of Gilgamesh', one of the world's most ancient legends concerning a mythical king of Uruk, tells of a man's quest for immortality. Written at the beginning of the 2nd millennium BC, the tale was embellished over time, expanding to 3,000 lines covering 11 stone tablets. Though Gilgamesh fails in his quest, the fact that his tale was written down has immortalised his exploits. His story includes several legends, like that of the Flood, which reappear in the Old Testament.

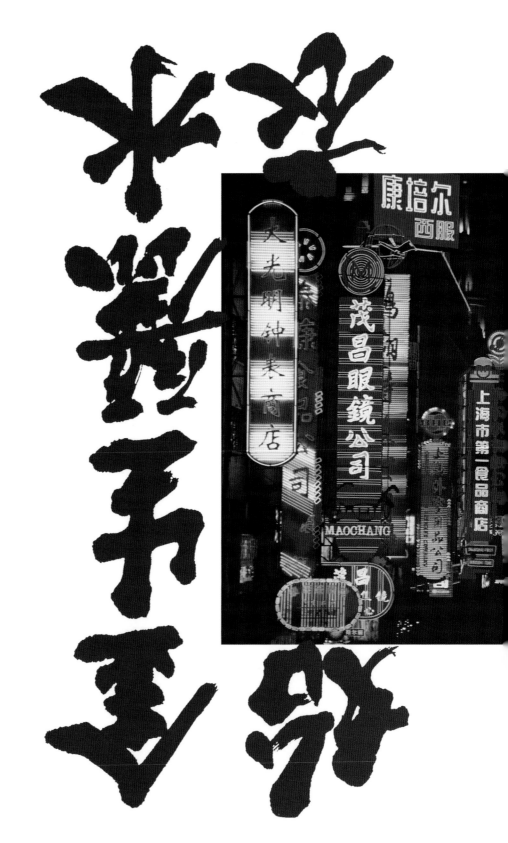

Towards an alphabet

Of all the earliest writing systems, only Chinese ideograms are still in current use. Their orthography was fixed and standardised in the 4th millennium BC and the symbols remained fundamentally the same right up to the writing reforms undertaken by the Chinese communist regime in 1956.

Unchanged by time
The passing of 30 centuries has done little to alter Chinese characters. The ideograms above, which date from the 6th century BC, are identical to those on the neon signs on a street in modern Shanghai.

Set in stone
Cuneiform tablets, like this seal (below) were widely used in Mesopotamia. The Rosetta Stone (below right) provided the key to deciphering hieroglyphics.

Egyptian hieroglyphics did not even survive to the end of the Pharaonic period. From the 3rd century BC, the Ptolemaic rulers of Egypt adopted the Greek alphabet. Hieratic script, one of several cursive Egyptian writing systems, continued to be used for copying religious texts, but even this fell into disuse after the 4th century AD, when the temples were closed and scribes dispersed.

Cuneiform script also had the disadvantage of being the preserve of an élite. When Babylon collapsed under repeated attacks by the Persian Empire, in 539 BC, the culture of ancient Mesopotamia was expunged and forgotten, and only rediscovered through the deciphering of Akkadian and Sumerian inscriptions between 1851 and 1905.

Before it entered its long spell in obscurity, cuneiform left behind for posterity the world's first alphabet, devised in Ugarit in Syria in around the 14th century BC. It was written left to right and comprised 30 consonant symbols, including three syllabic ones that represented vowels. This was a major advance as it gave people a set of phonetic symbols that enabled them to write whatever they wished.

The revolutionary new system was taken west by the Phoenicians, a trading people who inhabited the coast of Syria and the Lebanon at that time. These seafarers spread their alphabet, based on the one from Ugarit, throughout the Eastern Mediterranean. When the Greeks got hold of it, they refined it into their own alphabet, adding proper vowels. They ended up with the 24 letters of the Ancient Greek alphabet, which was firmly established by the 5th century BC. The home of democracy had thus furnished itself with a tool that enabled a greater number of people than ever before to read and write, to educate themselves and to articulate opinions.

Lost language
The language on this Cretan tablet (left), dating from c1500–1400 BC, is known as Linear B, which was only deciphered in the mid-20th century. Its precursor, Linear A, has yet to be decoded.

Newspeak *Mobile phones and text messaging have given rise to a new form of language that may itself, in time, fall into disuse and become unintelligible.*

CRACKING THE CODES

In 1822, Jean-François Champollion succeeded in deciphering Egyptian hieroglyphs. The breakthrough was made possible by the discovery in 1799 of the Rosetta Stone, a stele (stone slab) on which the same text had been carved in Egyptian hieroglyphs, in Demotic (a cursive Egyptian script used since the 3rd century AD) and in Ancient Greek. In the second half of the 19th century another trilingual inscription – this one carved into a rock at Benistun in the Zagros Mountains of Iran – enabled Henry Rawlinson, a lieutenant in the British army, to unravel the mystery of cuneiform. In 1952, the English scholar Michael Ventris deciphered Linear B, the writing system of the Cretans and Myceneans. Yet despite studying every language spoken in the Mediterranean for the last 4,000 years, Ventris failed to crack Linear A, an earlier Cretan script dated to c1750–1450 BC. Other scripts that continue to elude attempts to decode them are those of the Indus Valley civilisation that grew up at Mohenjo-Daro and Harappa in around 3000 BC and became one of the four great ancient centres of the written word.

The seal
c3200 BC

A long with writing, the Mesopotamians also invented letters, in the form of clay tablets, and envelopes. The latter were made of terracotta; to close them and authenticate their contents, they were stamped with a seal consisting of a small piece of polished stone with a design incised into its base. The seal left a relief imprint of this pattern on the damp clay of the envelope. The particular design revealed the identity of the sender.

Signed and sealed

Seals were stamped on official documents, diplomatic treaties and commercial transactions. They were also used for contracts between private individuals and, as such, are found in all ancient civilisations that were based on trade.

Each particular culture had its own type of seal. The Indus Valley civilisation is hallmarked by intaglio carvings of wildlife that decorate its steatite (soapstone) seals. The Minoan civilisation on Crete used the same material, which was easy to work, but carved it with written characters, the first Cretan hieroglyphs. The discovery of seals far from their place of origin is a sure sign of trade links or diplomatic relations between ancient cultures.

Great craftsmanship

The cultures that arose between the Tigris and Euphrates rivers were characterised by the cylinder seal. Rolling this type of seal across damp clay produces a kind of miniature fresco. The surface area of cylinder seals was greater than that of flat tablets, and their repertoire of images is far more extensive. The scenes from mythology, religion, war and daily life that appear on them provide researchers with invaluable information on how people lived. Cylinder seals were proof of a person's identity and were passed down from generation to generation.

Circular signature
A Sumerian cylinder seal from the 3rd millennium BC (left) and the impression it created (above).

Heavy stamp
A favourite material for seals in China was jade, but this one, dating from the Han Dynasty (200 BC–AD 220), is made of bronze. It is inlaid with gold and in the shape of a turtle, symbolising eternity.

THE ORIGINS OF PRINTING

Given the huge number of different symbols available in the Chinese script, it is easy to choose combinations of symbols that make a unique personal signature. Accordingly, Chinese seals, which were large and cube-shaped, were carved with individual combinations of pictograms. They were coated with ink and then used as stamps to make a mark on paper. They can lay claim to being the prototypes of the movable metal type pieces that came to be used many centuries later to compose lines of printed text.

WRITING MATERIALS
From stone to paper

By definition, writing cannot exist without the surface on which it appears. From cuneiform impressions in clay to ink on paper, the various materials that ancient peoples used to engrave, paint or draw scripts upon tell us a great deal about the civilisations that developed writing systems. People have been determined, quite literally, to leave their mark.

Egyptian exercise
An ancient Egyptian school book made of wooden boards. The script is hieratic, which developed from earlier hieroglyphs, but could be written in a cursive (joined-up) form more suited to writing on scrolls. For much of ancient Egyptian history, the hieratic script was contemporary with hieroglyphs, but was used for everyday tasks such as record-keeping and writing letters. It remained in use until the 26th Dynasty (6th–5th centuries BC).

The first surface on which people recorded facts for posterity was stone. On the walls of ancient Egyptian temples, for example, hieroglyphs relating the great deeds of the pharaohs were aimed at both a contemporary audience and future generations. Even in the innermost private recesses of burial chambers, the walls are inscribed with magical formulae designed to guide the soul of the deceased ruler safely into the afterlife. Stone, then, was the principal medium through which ancient Egyptian civilisation promoted its achievements and values. Hieroglyphic writing, which was standardised by about 2700 BC, reveals not just Egypt's history, but also its religious life, its art and its social mores.

In Mesopotamia, meanwhile, the most complete legal text to survive from ancient times, the 18th-century BC Code of Hammurabi, was also written on stone, carved onto a basalt stele preserved today in the Louvre in Paris.

Tablets and plaques

Yet most of our knowledge about ancient Mesopotamia comes not from records on stone but from clay tablets. Although many are extremely fragile or in pieces, these tablets contain a wide range of royal annals, from religious writings to medical and literary texts. Soft clay was kneaded and fashioned into tablets by the scribe, who always kept to hand balls of clay soaking in water, before being inscribed with a reed pen while the clay was still wet. Once the tablets had been filled with indented symbols, which made it easy for readers to run

their fingers along, they were dried in the sun or baked hard in an oven. Finally, the finished tablets were stacked, much like books nowadays, on the shelves of royal or private libraries.

From the start of the 2nd millennium BC, documents were also written on small plaques made either of wood or ivory covered with a wax film. Multiple plaques comprising a single work were sometimes joined in pairs using metal hinges. The resulting polyptych could be folded like a screen and was the ancestor of the book. Nevertheless, the clay tablet remained the favoured writing medium in Mesopotamia. This is hardly surprising, since the raw materials of clay and the reeds for making pens exist in abundance there. Moreover, cuneiform writing would not have taken the form it did had it not been written on soft clay, which made it impossible to draw graceful curves or intricate symbols. Straight lines were the order of the day, and the pen pressing into the clay naturally created the wedge shape.

Papyrus – gift from the gods

Papyrus was one of the many benefits that the Nile bestowed on ancient Egypt. From around 2500 BC, this plant provided scribes with an

Diverse media
Papyrus grows by the Nile (bottom right), but papyrus for writing was so costly the Egyptians used potsherds – pieces of broken pottery – for everyday messages (left). An 18th-century parchment scroll (bottom left) contains a copy of the Hebrew Torah. The image below shows Chinese paper-makers, also in the 18th century.

INVENTING INK

For drawing symbols on papyrus, Egyptian scribes used two colours of ink: black, the more commonplace, and red, which was reserved for writing the names of gods and invoking their favour. The thick black ink was made by mixing fat with gum arabic, a natural gum made from the sap of acacia trees. This was not far from the Chinese formula for ink, which combined ferrous sulphate with the sap of the lacquer tree. Red ink was made from either ochre or cinnabar (mercury sulphide). Ink took the form of a powder, which the scribe mixed with water to the required thickness.

ideal medium for their texts. The Egyptians also used it to make ropes, mats and sandals. Strips cut from the pith of papyrus stems were interwoven to form thick sheets of papyrus, which were then sliced, dried and buffed to yield a smooth and flat surface. Using a starch-based adhesive, these pages were glued together, end to end, to form a scroll. Papyrus was reserved for important texts: everyday messages were written either on flat stones or on pieces of pottery known as ostraca.

Reed pens – the ends of which were crushed to produce thin hairs like a paintbrush – ran smoothly across papyrus. Over time, as scribes wearied of painting laborious individual hieroglyphs, the symbols grew simpler and writing became cursive – symbols were joined up. Papyrus and writing in ancient Egypt is inextricably bound up with the priesthood.

Parchment and paper

Since it was in demand as an export, papyrus was extremely expensive. The Egyptians were also familiar with parchment, which was made from animal skin steeped in a lime bath then carefully rubbed with pumice. But making parchment was even more labour-intensive than papyrus, and it was only in the Middle Ages that it really came to supplant papyrus in western Europe. Meanwhile, in the 2nd century AD, the Chinese invented paper. This discovery saw writing become widespread as never before, yet it did not reach the West until the 12th century.

WINE – c3200 BC
Nectar of the gods

Along with beer, wine is one of the oldest man-made drinks. As early as 7000 BC, people in northern Iran are thought to have pressed wine from wild grapes. Some 4,000 years then elapsed before the emergence of true viticulture. Wines flavoured with additives, some of them surprising, became very popular in the ancient world.

Around 60 different species of vine are known to science, and these, in turn, have numerous varieties. One particular species, *Vitis vinifera*, bears fruit that, when fermented, produces wine. It first appeared after the end of the last Ice Age. As the Earth's climate grew milder, many plants began to flourish and spread throughout the warm, dry zones, especially in Central Asia and the Middle East. Botanists have identified several wild vine species in the Caucasus that are extremely close to *V. vinifera*, leading them to speculate that it may have originated in this part of the world.

It is likely that the first vines underwent natural hybridisation and possibly also successive human experiments with selective

Ancient art
As early as 1500 BC, the Egyptians had mastered winemaking (above). Later, the Romans processed grapes, as on this bas-relief (right), to produce some fine vintage wines.

breeding in an attempt to produce a variety most suited to making wine. The presence of grape pips at Palaeolithic sites from around 7000 BC indicates that vines were already being cultivated at that stage. On the other hand, there is no conclusive proof that humans truly mastered viticulture before the 6th millennium BC. In order to produce a regular crop of grapes, vines need to be pruned at the end of their dormant period. In the past, this would have happened naturally, as herds of goats and sheep browsed the new shoots every spring – indeed, this was one of the reasons for their domestication.

The first vineyard dates from at least 3200 BC, when the Egyptians (and possibly also the Phoenicians) began planting and tending vines by pruning them regularly every year. Barely two centuries later, wine-growing was well established in Mesopotamia and around the shores of the Black Sea.

The vintner's art

The first grapes were grown for eating, and the discovery of wine – the result of grape juice fermenting – most likely occurred by accident. It would only have taken ripe, juicy grapes a few hours in full sun for fermentation (the gradual transformation of natural fruit sugars into alcohol) to begin of its own accord, facilitated by natural yeasts on the 'bloom' of the fruit. Before long, wine was being made throughout the Mediterranean. Ancient methods of viticulture, illustrated in many relics of the period, were similar to those still in use today. Vines were pruned annually and grapes harvested in autumn. In Egypt, grapes were collected in wicker baskets, then trodden in huge wooden vats to get the fermentation process underway. Once crushed, the grapes – skins, juice and all – were poured into loosely corked earthenware jars to complete their fermentation. Finally, the mixture was filtered and flavoured before being stored in sealed amphorae. The grape was not the only fruit that produced wine: palm and date juice could be fermented in a similar way.

Acquired tastes

Although the business of growing grapes and making wine has changed little down the ages, the same cannot be said for the taste of the end product. People nowadays would be amazed at what passed for wine in antiquity. To help preserve wine, ancient growers added different ingredients to it, depending on the region: heavily sweetened date juice in Egypt; honey and spices in Greece; pepper in China.

The grape press
An illumination from a medical treatise by Aldebrande de Florence (1356) portrays a grape press in remarkable detail. Many medieval writers and scholars attributed therapeutic properties to wine.

Terracotta jars
First made by the Egyptians, terracotta amphorae were adapted by the Greeks and Romans many centuries later for transporting and storing wine.

A POPULAR 'POISON'

A Persian legend recounts how one of their ancient kings once filled a jar with grapes but then forgot all about them. When he did come to try them, he decided that they had been greatly improved by fermentation, but he refrained from consuming them all at once – and from telling others. To warn others off them, he had the word 'poison' inscribed on the jar. Yet it so happened that one of his concubines tried to do away with herself. She found the jar and drank its supposedly fatal contents. Not only did the 'poison' not kill her, she went straight to the king and told him how delicious it was. Persians liked to tell this story, with its happy ending, to show how people accidentally discovered the joys of being tipsy.

Fashionable taste
This glass carafe in the form of a bunch of grapes was made for a Romano-Gallic patrician of the 2nd century AD.

A way of life
A banqueting scene on a 4th-century BC Athenian vase shows wine being enjoyed at a ceremony in honour of its patron god Dionysus, also called Bacchus.

The Greeks, who did not like their wines to be too strong, diluted them with water, whereas the Romans had a preference for syrupy wines and complained about the bitter taste of wine from Gaul. In the Middle Ages, people tended to prefer full-bodied or fortified wines; these were stored in wooden casks, which were introduced by the Gauls in around 500 BC.

Over the course of the centuries, wines continued to evolve. New varieties were discovered that were better adapted to local climatic conditions, and more suitable locations for growing vines were also identified. Even in ancient Sumer, for instance, mountain wines cultivated on high-altitude vineyards were regarded as superior to those grown on the plain. Several centuries later, the Roman poet Virgil (70–19 BC) touched on the same subject when he claimed in his *Georgics* that 'vines prefer open, high ground'. From ancient times, merchant vessels plied the Mediterranean carrying a variety of different wines: Romans were particularly fond of wine from Pelusium, a wine-growing region in the Nile Delta, while the Greek inhabitants of Alexandria under the Ptolemies spared no expense to get hold of wines from their homeland.

Blight and salvation from the New World

All the grape varieties of Europe, from the ancient muscats of Greece to the pinot noirs grown in the abbeys of Burgundy, derived from the same species, *Vitis vinifera*, which had long been referred to simply as the 'European vine'. When the first colonists set foot in the New

TIPPLES FROM AROUND THE WORLD

The first settled farmers fermented a huge variety of plants to produce alcoholic drinks. In Mesopotamia, around 6,000 years ago, people steeped barley, wheat and millet in water-filled jars that were left exposed to sunlight. The heat acted on the natural yeasts in the grains to produce beer, which was then flavoured with herbs or date juice.

Similarly, in China some 4,000 years ago rice and millet were fermented to make a beer called *tchoo*. In the 9th century BC, in India and Sri Lanka, rice was brewed with either molasses or the sap of the palm tree to produce a drink called toddy (or arak in Sri Lanka) that is still made today. The

Japanese used rice on its own to make sake, which remains popular to this day. At about the same time, horse-riding nomads of Central Asia, such as the Tatars, and the people of the Caucasus fermented an alcoholic beverage from mare's milk known variously as koumiss or kefir, depending on the region.

In Central and South America, pulque was made from the sap of the agave plant; in modern times, this is still made in almost industrial quantities. It was reputed to enable people to converse with the gods. By fermenting honey with spices, the Maya made a sparkling drink

Kava-brewing ceremony on Fiji
Made from a plant of the same name, kava is brewed throughout the South Pacific. Its use is often associated with religious rites.

called *balche*. The Amerindian people of the Andes made many alcoholic drinks, of which the oldest is a corn-based drink called *chicha*, which is still brewed today.

New World …
In Central and South America, the pulp of the agave (right) is fermented into pulque.

… And Old
A statuette made during the Old Kingdom of ancient Egypt shows a woman brewing beer.

World, they found new species of vine growing on American soil, and duly set about trying to produce wine from them. The results were mediocre, and so they tried acclimatising the European vine to their new homeland, albeit without much success. The colonists had failed to notice that, although the American species were less well suited to making good wine, they had at least developed a remarkable resistance to a native parasite that attacked vinestocks, an insect called the grape phylloxera. This highly destructive aphid reached Europe at the beginning of the 20th century, with disastrous results. All the Old World vines were affected and almost completely wiped out in the space of just a few years.

Help was at hand from America. Scientists managed to develop healthy plants by grafting European varietals onto American rootstocks. These new plants were resistant to phylloxera, and they produced some extremely palatable grapes. All of today's Chardonnay and Cabernet Sauvignon vines, for instance, are the fruit of this rescue operation.

New vines produced by grafting or careful hybridisation have since created a huge choice of grape varieties for growers worldwide: reds or whites, early or late harvests, more or less floral, and more or less high-yielding. This has enabled growers outside the areas where vines were traditionally cultivated to select the best possible vine varieties to suit the amount of sunlight and rainfall in their region, as well as to produce the kind of taste they are hoping to achieve.

Modern winemaking techniques, such as micro-oxygenation, have made wines more standardised and reliable. This is good for the average wine-drinker, but some connoisseurs complain that the 'terroir', or unique local character, of certain wines has been spoilt or lost.

A global instrument

From c2700 BC, several types of flute existed in China, including the syrinx (Pan pipes), the recorder and a transverse flute with a mouthpiece in the centre. Finds from royal tombs in the Mesopotamian city of Ur prove that the Sumerians used double pipes (*zummara*), made from either silver or bulrushes. The long oblique flute (*ney*) of ancient Egypt, a rim-blown instrument without a mouthpiece, appeared sometime between the Old and Middle Kingdoms. Played exclusively by men, this deep-sounding flute (which had no semitones) soon became part of Egyptian orchestras, which already featured clarinets, trumpets, oboes, harps and drums. The Egyptians used the flute for many different purposes: to accompany religious ceremonies, to provide a steady rhythm for labourers in the fields, or simply for recreation.

Early evidence
A flute player accompanies dancers in an Aboriginal painting from Australia (above).

The flute
c3200 BC

The flute is one of the oldest known musical instruments. It almost certainly came about as a result of someone turning a reed, or a piece of bone, into a makeshift whistle – perhaps to imitate a bird, scare off a predator, raise the alarm, or drive away evil spirits. In Isturiz cave, in the Basque region of southwest France, archaeologists recently discovered what they believe to be the ancestor of all flutes. Dating from the start of the so-called Aurignacian culture of the Upper Palaeolithic (*c*22,000 BC), this instrument, carved from a bird bone, has the same basic pattern as instruments made some 14,000 years later, which have been found at various sites. The first pictorial representation of the flute – on an Egyptian plaque showing a flute player – occurs later still, in around 3200 BC.

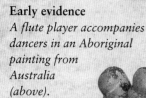

Chinese musician
A woman plays a set of Pan pipes in a statuette from the 7th century AD.

Palaeolithic flute
This instrument made of bone (right) was found in the Basque region of southern France.

THREE CENTURIES OF IMPROVEMENTS

The transverse flute was only 'rediscovered' in the 15th century, when it was incorporated into new forms of composition being developed at that time. In the 17th century a family of French musicians, the Hotteterres, came up with a major innovation in flute design. Hitherto made from a single block of wood, the flute was now divided into three sections; this enabled it to be tuned by sliding the top section up or down. In the early 18th century, a fourth detachable segment of varying length was added, which allowed the player to change the pitch. In 1821, the German flautist Theobald Böhm increased the range with a system of keys and levers that closed off or opened the instrument's soundholes.

The harp c3000 BC

It cannot have taken long for people to discover that a plucked string produces a sound as it vibrates. In the absence of any modulation, the sound remains a monotone. The harp is based on the idea that sounds can be modulated by using strings of different lengths. Although the scientific theory behind the principle was not expounded until Pythagoras in the 6th century BC, the earliest known harps – from Ur in Mesopotamia – are far older, dating from around 3000 BC. The instruments have six to eight strings attached to an arched upright, and were played sitting down or kneeling. The same basic pattern of instrument recurs in Old Kingdom Egypt. A defining characteristic of harps is that the strings lie perpendicular, not parallel, to the soundboard; scholars believe that the 'harp' famously played by King David of Israel was not a harp at all but a kind of lyre.

Made for music and dance

The Egyptians continued to play the arched harp, but it was supplanted in Mesopotamia by the angular harp (so called because of the angle between the neck of the instrument, to which the strings were attached, and the soundboard). In New Kingdom Egypt, the arched harp, or *bint*, evolved to take on a wide variety of different forms, most notably a large version with 20 strings, which was often lavishly decorated with floral and geometrical motifs.

The harp was ubiquitous in Egypt and throughout the ancient Near East, but was gradually abandoned by the Greeks and Romans in favour of the cithara and the lyre. In Mesopotamia, where music was considered a gift from the gods, the harp and other stringed instruments were widely used in religious rituals, accompanying singing, drumming and brass playing. The harp was a favourite recreational instrument for ladies of the ruling élite, who performed on it at family gatherings. It would also have been played at sacred dances, formal processions and funeral banquets.

Aegean art
Gazing skywards as if for inspiration, this statue of a harpist from Amorgos on the Cyclades Islands was made in around 2300 BC.

EVOLUTION OF THE HARP

The triangular frame harp or trigonon, with a forepillar, was developed in the late Egyptian New Kingdom. Known in Europe from the 8th century, it was the ancestor of many similar instruments, notably the Celtic harp, which had levers and hooks allowing the harpist to change the pitch of every string. From the Renaissance onwards, the harp evolved into a far more complex instrument that could play chromatic scales. After almost 150 years of constant refinement, it reached a peak in its development in 1811, when the French maker Sébastien Érard created the double-action pedal harp. On this instrument each string can play its neutral pitch along with its accompanying sharp and flat, just like a piano.

Eritrean harp
This modern-day instrument (below) is probably very similar in form and construction to the very first harps.

The growth of towns

Many stages marked the slow but inexorable evolution of human dwellings and settlements from makeshift prehistoric shelters, through tented encampments to small villages of wooden huts. Eventually, people began to live together in large numbers within walled cities.

Remains of ancient cities
The ruins of Uruk (below), an ancient Sumerian city in present-day Iraq, and a depiction of a ziggurat on a Mesopotamian cylinder seal dating from c1000 BC (right).

Uruk, which grew up in Lower Mesopotamia from around 3700 BC, displays all the typical characteristics of an ancient city. First and foremost, it was protected by a 9.5km-long defensive wall, which from *c*3000 BC was punctuated with no fewer than 900 towers set just 9 metres apart from one another. At its heart, the sacred quarter known as the Eanna not only celebrated the majesty of the city's tutelary goddess Inanna (also known as Ishtar) but also proclaimed the prowess of its builders. The temple dedicated to Inanna was sited at the top of a ziggurat, a tower reminiscent of the step pyramids of Egypt, comprising terraces of diminishing size; the lowest terrace measured 55 metres square. Leading up to the temple was a three-tiered staircase.

In common with all other buildings in Sumer, the Uruk ziggurat was constructed of mud bricks, although its builders devised ingenious ways of protecting the structure from the ravages of the weather. Reed matting was laid between the courses of brickwork to compensate for the gradual settling of the building, while guttering and other drainage systems channelled water away. In other ancient ziggurats, archaeologists have noted various ways in which the builders tried to make their structures more stable: terracotta facings encased large areas of mud-brick masonry;

THE ENIGMA OF JERICHO

Human dwellings did not evolve in a linear fashion, nor can the same criteria be applied universally. Mysteries remain, such as that of Jericho. We know that the city was surrounded by defensive walls in the 8th millennium BC. Their imposing proportions are described in the Old Testament: 3 metres wide and 4 metres high, with a spectacular tower 10 metres across rising up 4 metres above the wall to reach a total height of 8 metres. These were the famous walls that Joshua, Moses' general, led his army around, sounding trumpets to make them crumble. And yet these mighty ramparts protected dwellings that came from a much earlier era: halfway between a hut and a house, and partly subterranean, the typical circular dwellings of Jericho were relics of the Mesolithic Natufian culture, which thrived in northern Palestine in around the 11th millennium BC. Is seems scarcely plausible that, some 3,000 years later, such massive defences would have been built to protect such a modest settlement.

beams acted as ties from external to internal walls. The technique of building in stages was later used for domestic dwellings too.

Symbols of power and inequality

The system of urban organisation that would ultimately prevail throughout the ancient world was already evident at Uruk. Royal palaces, temples and residences of the ruling élite were built on raised terraces, dominating the lower city where the common people lived. Before long, the different trades among the craftsmen and merchant classes began to organise themselves by streets (*sûqu* in Akkadian, one of the languages of ancient Mesopotamia, from which comes the Arabic word *souk*). Thus the physical landscape of the city came to symbolise both the social hierarchy and people's roles within it. For while it is true to say that cities arose as a result of people congregating in a restricted space, their genesis is also closely linked to the emergence within farming communities of political and religious leaders. The ziggurats of Mesopotamia or the pyramids of Egypt are emblematic of the growing concentration of power that sparked the 'urban revolution'.

The golden age of city-states – Mari, Ebla and Ugarit

In 1933, Bedouin tribesmen digging at a site on the banks of the Euphrates in Syria chanced upon the ruins of the ancient city of Mari. This Sumerian city was established during the first third of the 3rd millennium BC and sank into obscurity after being sacked by King Hammurabi of Babylon in 1759 BC. The site has yielded some remarkable archaeological treasures. It was evident that a highly advanced civilisation had developed there, stimulated by an economic boom based on control of the trade in minerals and timber.

Mari was served by two canals: one canal provided the city with its water supply, the other was used for navigation. A circular earth dyke protected the city from the seasonal flooding of the Euphrates. The city centre comprised administrative and religious buildings, along with an imposing royal palace. This latter building housed several alabaster statues depicting standing figures with their

Buildings on a grand scale
A reconstruction of the layout of Mari in what is now Syria (above). The Great Ziggurat of Ur (below) was built in the 3rd millennium BC. This artist's impression shows how it would have looked in its heyday.

Faded glory
*The foundations
of Hattusa, the
former capital
of the Hittite
Empire, are
laid out plain
to see in what
is now Turkey.*

Ancient technology
*The shaduf (below)
has been in use in
Egypt since ancient
times as a means to
raise water for
irrigation.*

hands clasped across their chests, displaying a hitherto unknown degree of sculptural realism.

Together with Mari, Ebla was the greatest kingdom in the region in the 3rd millennium BC. Its influence spread far and wide across the Syrian steppe. The city owed its prosperity to the export of woollen cloth and to trade in timber, silver and copper. The royal palace,

VITAL RESOURCE

The cities of the Fertile Crescent needed water not just for gardens, such as the famous Hanging Gardens of Babylon, but also for their inhabitants to cook with and wash in. Ways and means had to be devised to channel water to where it was needed.

Counterweighted devices for lifting water are known to have existed from the 3rd millennium BC. They worked on the same principle as the shaduf, a weighted and pivoted pole-and-bucket arrangement. Using such simple but ingenious machines, the ancient Mesopotamians transferred water to irrigation ditches. In the main, these took the form of open trenches, but some underground canals were dug to channel water directly into wells that supplied palaces and private houses with their daily water needs.

Drains and sewers carried away waste water. The oldest have been found at the settlement of Habuba Kabira in Syria, dating from 3100 BC, followed by those at Mari (also in Syria) and Tell Asmar in Iraq. At Mohenjo Daro in the Indus Valley, a network of drains and settling tanks served the entire city by the 3rd millennium BC.

controlled by a king assisted by a minister, presided over a system that centralised the harvests and rearing of flocks of sheep, and redistributed the accrued wealth. This new and highly rational administrative model would be replicated in many other places.

The Canaanite port of Ugarit, in today's Syria, grew rapidly from the end of the 2nd millennium BC. The city expanded considerably, acquiring a new outer ring of defences, streets arranged in a grid pattern and, naturally, a royal palace and several temples. Its citizens, who had grown wealthy through trade with Egypt and other states around the Mediterranean, had a taste for bronze and silver artefacts and gold jewellery. The city continued to prosper until it was destroyed by an earthquake in the 13th century BC.

Çatal Hüyük and Lepenski Vir
Further back in prehistory, two sites emerge as the precursors of cities. From around 7000 BC, at the start of the Mesolithic period, Çatal Hüyük (in modern Turkey) and Lepenski Vir on the River Danube were major population centres, with significant numbers of people inhabiting structures that prefigured those of later cities. Çatal Hüyük is thought to have housed around 1,000 families, or some 5,000 people all told, on a site covering almost 13 hectares: these statistics alone justify its designation as a town, even though certain features remain distinctly primitive. For instance, there are no defensive walls around Çatal Hüyük and few streets and gates, and the houses were accessed through holes in the ceiling. The dwellings were typically small, averaging just 25 square metres for the family living space, plus a storeroom for food and

other supplies. Archaeologists have uncovered what they think are shrines, pointing to an emergent civilisation based on religion, though the smooth plastered walls make them virtually indistinguishable from living quarters.

Communal building

Delving still further back in time, before the first permanent villages, archaeology has identified encampments comprising the most rudimentary shelters and basic forms of social organisation. Through all these early phases of communal living, from simple bivouacs made of branches to tents, wooden huts and finally permanent houses, humans learnt the advantages of living in family units and working as a group.

One striking example of communal endeavour and people's ability to adapt to their environment are the huts built around 35,000–10,000 BC by mammoth hunters of the Upper Palaeolithic. The huts are found mainly in Eastern Europe, where the forests gave way to steppe. At Mezhirich, in the Ukraine, five such huts have come to light, all built to the same circular pattern, with a diameter of around 6 metres. They comprise a framework of mammoth tusks supported by foundations made from piles of skulls and jawbones. The whole frame was covered with larger bones with hides still attached to them. It took the carcases of 20 mammoths to

Frame construction
Villagers in Burkina Faso (above) erect a hut by lashing together poles to make a frame, which is then covered with animal hides.

Early dwellings
An artist's reconstruction of stilt houses on Lake Chalain near Geneva, Switzerland (above), and a prehistoric mammoth bone-and-hide hut (below).

build such a structure. The encampment was almost certainly occupied, at least on a semi-permanent basis, by an organised group of hunters.

The constant need for security

From the same period, camps in western Europe show that people there were beginning to gather in groups. At Pincevent, in the French département of Seine-et-Marne, a dozen or so groups of dwellings have been discovered, dating from the Upper Palaeolithic. The constructions were lightweight wooden-framed tents covered with skins, suited to the needs of a transient community during the reindeer-hunting season, but they still represented a semi-permanent settlement. Domestic tasks took place around the hearths near the entrances of the tents, while people bedded down behind the fires. Outside, set some way apart from the tents, were places for skinning animals and treating the hides.

Lower Palaeolithic encampments have been on an altogether smaller scale, with less of a standardised layout, though the actual construction techniques were very

when people found ready-made natural shelters, like caves or cliff overhangs, they still felt it necessary to erect lean-to shelters against the rockface.

Farming and cities

The concept of towns seems to have arisen sometime between the 7th and 3rd millennia BC. A major factor in their growth was the momentous climatic change that took place from around 10,000 BC, as the great ice sheets that had covered much of the Earth began to melt. Glaciers receded, the climate became milder, plants flourished and rivers and other watercourses swelled. As people turned to agriculture and systematic animal husbandry, they moved from a nomadic or semi-nomadic hunter-gatherer way of life to a settled one.

People moved progressively from encampments to villages, and from villages to towns. The early farmers did not yet know the principle of crop rotation and leaving fields fallow, and so, having exhausted the soil, they had to find new areas to cultivate. Mastery of irrigation, especially at favourable sites along the Nile, Tigris and Euphrates, where floods regularly enriched the soil with silt, entailed building more durable structures.

And so there arose, some 1,500 years after the end of the last Ice Age, Çatal Hüyük, Lepenski Vir and dozens of other settlements that were not yet cities but were more than

Ancient settlement
Jerf el-Ahmar (above) was originally sited on the Middle Euphrates in Syria. It was moved before the valley was flooded after construction of the Tishrin Dam in 1998.

similar: a framework of branches, bent and tied at the apex and anchored to the ground with stones, then covered at first with leaves and later with hides. This was the universal pattern for the prehistoric hut. The earliest example of such a dwelling is a stone circle, around 5 metres in diameter, discovered in the Olduvai Gorge in Tanzania and estimated to be 1.8 million years old. This find seems to indicate that, from the very earliest times, humans felt the need to mark out a living space and protect themselves while they slept; even

Reed buildings
A typical village of the Marsh Arabs of Iraq and the interior of a traditional mudhif *or guest house (inset).*

A WINDOW ON THE PAST – THE HOUSES OF THE MARSH ARABS

An extensive area of marshland covering some 12,000 square kilometres to the north of the city of Basra in Iraq, near the confluence of the Tigris and Euphrates rivers, is home to tribes of hunters and fishermen called the Madan. These people, more commonly known as the Marsh Arabs, have lived in the region for thousands of years, and they still keep alive a remarkable tradition of domestic architecture in the form of reed-built structures. The structures are of two kinds, the *raba* (house) and the *mudhif* (guesthouse). Both appear to rise straight out of the water and look as though they have been in place since the dawn of time. They are built using knowledge and techniques passed down from one generation to the next.

The reeds in the marshes can grow up to 8 metres tall and are transported to the site on a *balam*, a raft some 10 metres long. The most striking feature of the *mudhif* is its barrel-vaulted roof, like the hull of an upturned boat. Long bunches of reeds are bent over to form the framework of the building; these are then covered with matting. Open-weave mats, sometimes with holes designed into their pattern, form the windows. Reeds make up the entire fabric of the building, which contains no nails, rope or wire. Though the interior of a *mudhif* is very sparsely furnished, with just beds or sleeping mats and a few storage chests, the Marsh Arabs set great store by offering guests generous hospitality.

Mud-brick town
The town of Huth in northern Yemen (left) still has houses built of mud bricks. The bricks have been used as a construction material for thousands of years in the arid Middle East and North Africa.

villages. After another 4,000 years, the history of towns truly began with the rise of Uruk, the template for all other Mesopotamian cities.

From hides to mud and brick

Throughout the Middle East, be it in Mesopotamia, the Indus Valley or Egypt, all the earliest buildings were made of mud bricks. Clay was readily available from riverbanks and was easy to work, but the end product was not very durable. To make mud bricks less fragile, straw or bitumen were added. The bricks were rarely fired, since this required wood, which was in very short supply in these arid regions. This type of house was exported to Europe from the Near East at around the same time as settled farming. But right from the outset it was adapted to local conditions: flat roofs, for instance, gave way to pitched roofs, which were better suited to areas of high rainfall.

Greece was a special case. In Sesklo, one of Europe's oldest known villages, dating from *c*6000 BC, the houses were made of mud bricks, but had stone foundations. Later, a Mediterranean pattern of house, built of dry stone and found principally in the south of France and Spain, became widespread.

From the 5th century BC, the Danubian culture spread from the north of Hungary right across central Europe as far as northern France, bringing with it a characteristic style of dwelling. The principal building material was timber, which comprised the basic framework. The wooden posts gave the walls their structural strength and the gaps in between were filled in with wattle (interwoven sticks), which formed a base for a plaster coat of mud known as daub. These half-timbered houses were roofed with thatch, and were invariably built side-on to the prevailing wind.

The ard – forerunner of the modern plough

The ard, the first true tool developed for farming, consisted of two joined pieces of wood pulled by a pair of draught animals. The name comes from Latin *aratrum*, but the origins of the ard go back far beyond Roman times. We know, for example, that it was used by the Egyptians and Mesopotamians in the 4th millennium BC.

Mesopotamian cylinder seals from the 4th millennium BC show peasants tilling the land with the aid of an ard. The appearance of this tool marked a turning point in the history of agriculture. Humans had known how to cultivate cereals since Neolithic times, but the only implements they had for turning the soil or digging holes for planting were simple hand-held digging-sticks or wooden spades that they pushed down with their feet. Tools that are still used today on some Pacific islands and in parts of Africa closely resemble the digging-sticks that preceded the plough.

From hoe to ard

Almost universally, digging-sticks were used in conjunction with the hoe, once that implement made its appearance in the 5th millennium BC. In all likelihood, people would have got the idea for the hoe from the forked branches of trees. Despite being hardened by fire, hoe blades remained rough-and-ready implements that were awkward to use.

Flint hoe
A hoe blade from Mesopotamia, made of flint. The blade would have been attached to a handle when it was used around 6000 BC.

Digging with a stick
A farmer from the Trobriand Islands in Melanesia working in his plot of yams.

Eventually, someone hit upon the idea of harnessing animal power to loosen the soil and turn it over. Basically, the ard was a harnessed hoe. It heralded a new phase of human history, as it enabled people to dig furrows over larger tracts of land, to improve crop yields and to greatly expand the area of land under cultivation. This technological innovation also stimulated momentous changes in people's way of life, giving rise to an increasingly settled lifestyle and the first large communities.

Sowing and ploughing

The ard appeared in Mesopotamia and Egypt at roughly the same time – the start of the Bronze Age. It probably spread to Europe, China and the Far East at a later date, though some archaeologists think that it may have been developed more or less simultaneously in different parts of the world. Made from wood, the tool took a variety of forms depending on the particular culture and era,

although the basic principle remained the same. The ard was shaped roughly like a 'V', one arm of which formed the stilt, which the ploughman held to steer, while the other arm formed the draught-pole – the long wooden shaft (curved to varying degrees) linking the ard to the yoke worn by the draught animals. The wedge-shaped base of the stilt, known as the sole, was fitted with a ploughshare made from either flint or iron; this was the business end of the ard, which cut into the sod.

Ploughing generally involved three separate operations. A first pass by the ard would roughly break up the ground and grub up roots. A second pass then reduced clods of earth to a finer soil. Finally, a third pass created furrows to sow seed in (or alternatively to bury seed that had already been sown on the surface of an unploughed field). Ard-ploughed furrows tended to be shallow: prior to the invention of the coulter (a vertical blade in front of the share

that opened up the soil) in the 4th century AD, the share only pushed a small amount of loosened earth up on either side of the furrow. To open up the furrow, early ploughmen had to heel the ard over slightly to one side or the other as they went along.

On the Mesopotamian ard, the draught pole was harnessed to a yoke worn on the withers (shoulders) of a pair of oxen. The ard itself comprised a transverse bar fitted with a fire-hardened wooden share and two stilts that the ploughman used to guide it. This type of plough spread throughout the Mediterranean. An image on a cylinder-seal *c*1500 BC shows a ploughman sowing seed by tipping it into a funnel that runs down to the sole of the ard.

Egypt ploughs its own furrow

The Egyptian ard, depicted in numerous hieroglyphs and on the walls of *mastaba* tombs, was unusual in having its components lashed together rather then jointed. As a result, it was not used in the same way as similar tools elsewhere; basically, the Egyptians sowed before they ploughed. This method, which

Division of labour
A mural from the tomb of Sennedjem in the necropolis at Deir el-Medina, Egypt, made in c1885 BC, shows him tilling the soil while his wife sows the grain. The ard depicted was of a kind widely used in ancient Egypt.

Simple hoe
Made from wood and rope, this modern replica is probably much like the tool used by Egyptian peasants around 3000 BC.

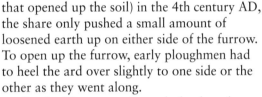

SEPARATING WHEAT FROM CHAFF

To thresh cereals, ancient Mesopotamians used an implement that the Romans called a *tribulum*. It consisted of a wooden framework, with pieces of flint or metal fitted to the underside, which was hauled over the harvested crop to separate the edible part of the grain from the chaff. This threshing-sledge would sometimes have a compartment on top, where the driver of the oxen or mules pulling it would stand. The Egyptians also used animals to thresh grain, by simply getting herds of cattle or mules to trample ears laid out on a firm floor.

astonished many Greek travellers, is explained by the annual flooding of the Nile, which deposited rich alluvial silt on riverside fields. Farmers could sow directly into this loose, fertile soil without needing to plough beforehand. All they had to do was to go over the ground lightly with a hoe, or even just get a herd of sheep to trample the sown ground. The ard, pulled by cattle or oxen, was simply used to cover up the grain afterwards.

Three models, two methods

In Europe and Scandinavia, the ard had just a single stilt. Over time, in lands from western Europe to India, three major types of ard developed. The bow-ard was closest to the primitive form of the implement, with the stilt and the draught pole formed from two curved pieces of timber. The sole-ard, which was widely used by the Greeks and Romans and particularly suited to tilling light, sandy soils, was recognisable by its elongated sole with a separate stilt

mounted at the back. Finally, the crook-ard had the stilt mortised directly into the draught-pole, which then curved down sharply to meet the sole. Much later, in around the 4th century AD, northern Europe saw the introduction of ards fitted with a coulter, an iron blade that helped to break up large clods in front of the share; these were customarily used for an initial pass over rough ground.

Ploughing itself is carried out by one of two methods. Flat tillage, which is particularly suited to Mediterranean soils, follows a symmetrical pattern in which the clods of earth are always thrown up towards the same side of the field. Another method, often used to drain heavy, damp soils, is asymmetrical or ridge tillage: the 'ridges' in question being the small heaps of earth that the ploughshare deposits to left and right with every pass of the plough.

From the ard to the plough

Rather than a transition from one technology to the other, the ard and the plough existed side by side for centuries. The ard was used mainly for shallow ploughing, and was notable for the symmetry of the furrows it created. The plough, which

Long-lasting tool
The ancient ard, shown right with its basic parts labelled, is still used in many parts of the world, such as the Indonesian island of Bali (below).

Stilt

Draught-pole

Sole

ALIEN TO AMERICA

The ard was unknown in pre-Columbian America, even though maize had been grown there since at least 2500 BC. In the 16th century, at the time of the Spanish conquest, indigenous peoples were still tilling the soil using hoes with stone blades. To make furrows for sowing seeds, the Incas of Peru used a digging-stick known as a *taccla*, which was tipped with copper. It looked very much like a spade, since it also had a bar for the foot to press down upon.

Hard work
The Greek vase painting above, from around 800 BC, shows oxen pulling an ard with a tall stilt and a long sole; the ploughman pressed down on the sole with his foot to deepen the furrow. The farmer ploughing a field with a team of horses below is using a double-handed plough, which gives him better control for deep tillage.

allowed the farmer to dig deeper into the soil and so gain higher crop yields, was effectively responsible for ushering in modern agriculture.

The sole-ard was inherently unstable and proved unsuitable for ridge tillage, since this entailed it working constantly on a slope. Small wonder, then, that the move away from the ard in favour of the plough began among the Celts of northern Europe, where soils were generally heavy and waterlogged and therefore benefited from ridge tilling. The plough retained the stilt, draught-pole and sole of the ard, but added wheels at the front, which made it more stable, and handles, which gave the ploughman more control. Deep ploughing brought into play a whole range of different components, such as the skim-coulter, which skims stones off the soil before it is turned; the coulter, which breaks up large clods of earth; the share, which lifts up the soil; and the mouldboard, which turns it over. The share and the mouldboard formed a single unit in later ploughs, fixed to the side of the draught-pole. Over time, the plough underwent numerous improvements, notably the movable

mouldboard, which made the ploughman's task far easier by allowing him to reposition it alternately on either side of the draught-pole as he went up and down the field.

The medieval 'green revolution'

Agriculture experienced ongoing expansion in the Middle Ages. The heavy mouldboard plough, which first appeared in around the 11th century, played a key role in the growth of farming in Europe, as forests were progressively cut down to make room for fields and areas of wasteland were ploughed up and turned over to cultivation. The landscape changed dramatically, as traditional broad fields gave way to long strips of land. The double Brabant plough, with two mouldboards set one above the other, and later the Canadian plough, with multiple shares, further boosted the performance of the implement. By the 1930s and 1940s, ploughs were being drawn by tractors in place of horses. Even so, the ard, which was ideally suited to poor, stony soils, remained in use in parts of Europe right up to the 1950s.

Brooches
c3000 BC

The earliest brooches, which appeared in the Bronze Age, closely resemble our modern safety pin. They were made of either bronze, gold or silver, and ranged from the very plain to the elaborately decorated. In the 1st century BC, the Romans invented the hinged fibula, with a body made of bronze, but a pin and clasp of iron to make it more durable. Brooches were functional items, used to fasten a person's cloak on the shoulder or to keep a cape in place, but they were also decorative. Crafted in a variety of forms, they often became pieces of jewellery in their own right, embellished with insets of enamel, gemstones or coral. Celtic brooches were beautiful high-status artefacts, set with enamel or coloured glass, or engraved with pictures of animals or geometric patterns on a cruciform base.

Ancient pin
A brooch from Greece made in about 700 BC.

Soap c3000 BC

A Sumerian clay tablet from the 3rd millennium BC is inscribed with a recipe for fat and lye (obtained from wood ash). The end product was used as a remedy for skin complaints and as a cleansing agent. Mesopotamians were not alone in appreciating the cleansing properties of oil or fat mixed with potash salts. In Egypt a hydrated form of sodium carbonate called natron, which occurred naturally in salt lakes, was mixed with a paste of ash and potassium-rich clay to produce a substance used to wash linen.

Neither the Greeks, who used the foam produced by the soapwort plant (*Saponaria*), nor the Romans knew about soap. The formula was 'rediscovered' by the Gauls, who hit upon the idea of mixing goat tallow, beechwood ash and herbs to produce a soft soap. The Roman historian Pliny the Elder reports that this Gaulish soap quickly caught on in the Roman world. The Roman physician Galen prescribed soap for removing impurities from the body, but it was the beginning of the 2nd century AD before people began to use it regularly to wash themselves and their clothes. Harder soap appeared in the 7th century, when the Arabs came up with a version made from a mixture of ash from sodium-rich seaweeds (which they called *al-qali*, the source of the word 'alkali') and fatty matter, occasionally enriched with vegetable oil. The famous Aleppo soap from Syria, perfumed with bay leaves, was made and sold from the 12th century onwards.

Marseilles soap
Soap with olive oil was made in Marseilles from the 13th century. It was the forerunner of white Castile soap, prized from the late 16th century.

Mirrors
c3000 BC

According to a famous legend of ancient Greece, Narcissus fell in love with his reflection in a pool. For countless thousands of years, this must have been the only way for early humans to look at themselves. By around 3000 BC, the Egyptians were using thin plates of gold, silver or bronze as mirrors. Polished to a reflective sheen, they were often set with precious stones and given handles; one well-preserved example was found at Medinet el-Ghorab.

The peoples of the Middle East and the Etruscans of Italy used thin slivers of obsidian, a volcanic glass, for the same purpose. The Romans carried on the Etruscan tradition of producing metallic mirrors, with lavish engravings and decoration on the back and equipped with handles made of ivory or rare woods. In the 1st century BC, they designed upright dressing mirrors with feet; known as 'psyches', they were the last word in refined Roman décor.

Reflective disc
The surface of this bronze Egyptian hand-mirror of around 1500 BC would have been polished to a high sheen.

MIRROR, MIRROR, MADE OF GLASS

The Romans improved the reflective qualities of metallic mirrors by covering them with glass, but the next great advance did not come until the 15th century, when the glassmakers of Nuremberg discovered the process of tinning. This involved coating the glass with a layer of tin and mercury by dipping it into a molten bath of the amalgam. The Venetians took over the process and jealously guarded the secret for two centuries. The definitive breakthrough came in 1835, when German chemist Justus von Liebig invented silvering, which entailed bonding a thin film of silver onto a sheet of glass. Today, aluminium is used, but the technique retains the name 'silvering'.

Wigs c3000 BC

Wigs first appeared in Egypt in the 4th millennium BC. The Egyptians were sticklers for personal hygiene and they adopted wigs to combat infestation by fleas, which could thrive only on people's real hair and their scalps. Decorative hairpieces, worn by men and women alike in ancient Egypt, were made more or less elaborate depending upon whether they were for everyday or ceremonial use. Made from real human hair, horsehair or dyed plant fibres stuck onto a canvas skullcap, wigs were taken off at night and placed on a stand. They would be combed through with a perfumed oil to keep them glossy. The wig performed an important social function in ensuring that members of the ruling élite were decorously attired in public, but it was also subject to the whims of fashion. In the 18th Dynasty, for instance, the short style of wig known as the Nubian (an 'urchin cut' in modern terms) was supplanted by long, curly wigs. Wigs remained popular in the ancient world, with Assyrians, Phoenicians, Greeks and even Romans wearing them. They fell out of favour for centuries and only came back into fashion after 1600. Their heyday in western Europe was the 17th and 18th centuries.

Fasionable hair
Long wigs were the height of fashion during Egypt's 18th Dynasty (14th century BC).

Forging ahead into a new metal age

Bronze, an alloy of copper and tin, probably came into being by accident in around 3000 BC. The advent of bronze-working gave people the wherewithal to make new weapons and tools, representing an important milestone in the development of technology. It also gave fresh impetus to the onward march of civilisation and trade.

Mastering the craft
Great skill is already evident in these two ancient artefacts: a terret, or rein guide, from a chariot (above) and a figurine of a woman making an offering to the gods (right).

Imagine the scenario. Some 12,000 years ago a group of hunter-gatherers move slowly along the banks of the Euphrates, through the lush vegetation that borders the river. One of the men stoops to pick up an unusual green stone that he spots on the riverbed. Out of sheer curiosity, he scratches it with his flint spearhead – and reveals a flash of reddish gold. Excitedly, he shows his find to his companions. Wading into the river in search of more of the new treasure, they find the sandy river bed liberally strewn with the strange rocks. That evening, back at camp, they introduce the rest of the tribe to their discovery. Perhaps this, or something very like it, was how one of history's great leaps forward was triggered.

Bronze bull
A bronze bull's head, made in the heyday of the Sumerian civilisation, would have decorated a piece of furniture or possibly a harp in around 2500 BC.

BIRTH OF AN INDUSTRY

The discovery of copper gave rise to the world's first truly significant mining industry. The oldest known copper mines are at Ain Buna, in Bulgaria, and Rudna Glava in Serbia, both of which date from the 5th millennium BC. Yet it was only with the dawn of the Bronze Age, which triggered a huge increase in demand for copper as a raw material, that copper-mining really took off across Europe and elsewhere. Such was the scale of the bronze industry that local foraging for surface copper deposits could no longer supply demand. Pits were sunk, some descending to depths of more than 100 metres. This in turn meant instituting safety measures, such as propping up the roof and walls of the shafts with timbers to prevent them caving in. The earliest copper mine in the world where wooden timbers were used for support is in the Jiangxi Province of China, at the ancient Tongling copper mine. To loosen the mineral-bearing rocks at the working face of the seam, miners would first light a fire and then douse it with cold water, causing the rock to split. They would then hack chunks off with hammers and picks.

Copper blazes a trail

The rocks on the Euphrates riverbed were nuggets of pure, or 'native', copper – a metal that was to have a profound impact on history. One of the most significant properties of copper is its malleability. By hammering pieces of copper with a stone, people found that they could fashion it into small pieces of useful jewellery, such as pins or brooches. And the more the copper was hit, the harder it became. Little by little, as people became more adept at working copper, metallurgy was born.

Copper did not just exist in a 'native' state. Often it occurred in the form of ores, mixed with rock and other minerals. In the 1960s, the remains of relatively sophisticated ancient furnaces were discovered at Tal-el-Iblis in Iran. These indicated that as early as 4000 BC people were extracting copper by heating the green mineral, malachite. It is something of a miracle that people came up with the idea at all, since copper ores give no outward sign of the riches they contain.

Copper smelting set in train a whole new metalworking industry. A range of weapons and tools – such as daggers, javelin heads, arrow shafts, hatchets, knives and chisels – was being produced from copper in Egypt by 5000 BC, while copper axes were being made and used in the Balkans before 3000 BC. Cyprus was the main supplier of copper in the ancient world – indeed, the word copper derives from the Latin word *cyprium*, after the island's name.

The new technology did not immediately supplant the tried and tested polished flint; after all, copper was neither very durable nor very easy to obtain. Copper implements bent on impact, so at first the metal was used for decorative objects. But copper's heyday was still to come.

Bronze appears on the scene

In around 3000 BC, once again in Mesopotamia, a revolutionary step was taken when the Sumerians chanced upon a new alloy of copper – bronze. There is no evidence to tell us precisely how this came about, but we can piece clues together and imagine the scene. A blacksmith, his face blackened by smoke, is working away at the roaring furnace of his forge in the city of Ur on the banks of the Euphrates, an area rich in copper deposits. Touching the tip of a knife that he has just turned out of a terracotta mould with two drain-holes, he notices that it is much harder than the knives he usually makes. Could the improvement be down to the new supplies of copper he has just started to get from a new mine? He has not done anything different from his usual working method, so decides the new supplies must be the answer – and smiles at his good fortune. From now on, he will use nothing else and his tools will soon gain a reputation for being the best in town.

An array of weapons
Bronze pike blades and swords from Lorestan, in present-day Iran, dating from the 2nd millennium BC.

Warrior gear

Arms and armour from Bronze Age Europe include a shield (c1200 BC) found in Oxfordshire, a helmet (c1000 BC) recovered from the bed of the Saône River in eastern France, and a 3,000-year-old hatchet unearthed at Vucedol in the Balkans.

Lucrative but deadly

Our blacksmith would have been unaware that the copper he was using was not, in fact, pure copper but had a significant quantity of another element (arsenic) mixed in with it, as did many of the copper ores from the region. In any event, the very first form of bronze was an alloy of copper and arsenic. The advantages of the alloy were clear from the start. It was easier to cast than pure copper, forming none of the bubbles that spoiled copper artefacts by making them more fragile. It was also more durable, enabling blacksmiths to turn out virtually indestructible tools: if tools got bent or blunted, they could be reforged. There was no doubt that bronze was a superior material.

The blacksmith of Ur must have paid dearly for his discovery and enhanced reputation, as smelting the arsenic-laced ore released highly toxic vapours that most likely killed him.

Many like him probably died before people discovered the cause. But by then, the basic lesson must have been learned: that the inherent flaws of pure copper could be overcome by alloying it with other metals.

An accidental additive

Quite how people discovered that the addition of tin made copper alloys superior to those involving arsenic – without releasing any deadly fumes into the bargain – is a mystery. Tin is rare in both Europe and the Middle East. Even so, the Royal Tombs at Ur contain a number of objects that are made from almost perfect bronze – that is, with a tin content of around 10 per cent. It seems likely that the Sumerians obtained their tin from the

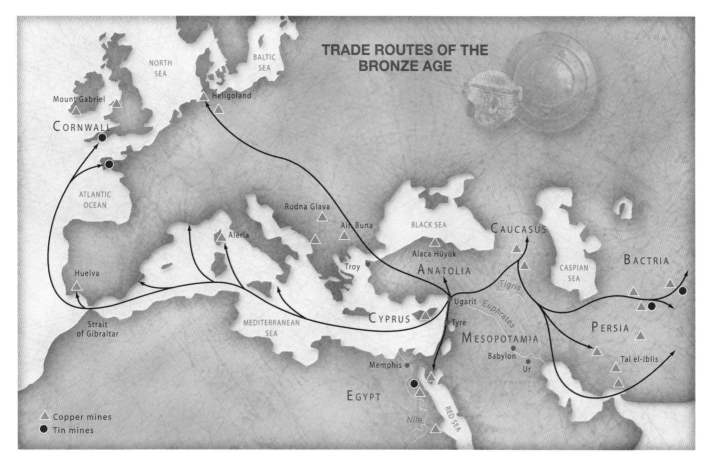

TRADE ROUTES OF THE BRONZE AGE

△ Copper mines
● Tin mines

Caucasus, which had both tin and copper in abundance. Indeed, it is the people of this region, who were both miners and gifted blacksmiths, who are the most likely to have invented tin-based bronze, at the beginning of the 3rd millennium BC. It may have come about through someone confusing malachite and cassiterite, the two commonest mineral ores of copper and tin respectively. In this part of the world, the ores even occur together in some deposits. A Caucasian blacksmith might well have inadvertently smelted them together.

Rapid spread

By the end of the 3rd millennium BC, bronze was renowned throughout the known world. Ur was one of the first city-states to have tin-based bronze in great quantities, but other cities were also quick to adopt it. Exquisitely engraved bronze artefacts have been found in the royal tombs of the Pre-Hittite rulers of Alacahüyük in central Anatolia, while in the late 19th century excavations by the German archaeologist Heinrich Schliemann at the site of the ancient city of Troy unearthed several bronze receptacles and weapons inlaid with lapis lazuli, dating from around 2400 BC.

The reason for this abundance of bronze objects in areas where tin does not naturally occur is, of course, trade, which grew exponentially during this period. By *c*2000 BC,

an extensive trading network ran from Afghanistan in the east to Sardinia, Sicily and Spain in the west. To the north, it spread as far as the shores of the Baltic Sea and to Cornwall. As diverse peoples exchanged cultural influences and technical know-how, Cornwall became famous as a source of tin.

Eventually, bronze became known throughout the whole of Europe. The first European metalworkers to emerge were the people of the so-called Bell Beaker culture (*c*2800–1900 BC), whose name derives from a particular type of ceramic vessel, shaped like an upside-down bell, found in their graves. Originally from Spain, these people were master potters and blacksmiths. But they were also merchants, criss-crossing Europe with their wares and spreading the use of bronze.

Trade routes
The technical skills of bronze-working spread from the Near East to Europe, forging new trade routes and uncovering new sources of raw materials.

Funerary effigy
A bronze head and hands sculpted as a symbolic reminder of a deceased Etruscan in the 7th century BC.

Into a new era – the Bronze Age

As a result of improving trade links, people's living standards began to improve. The changes wrought by the advent of the new technology were so momentous that it gave its name to the entire period: the Bronze Age.

Powerful cities grew up along the main routes that traders used to export the metal. One of the mightiest was the city of Troy in Asia Minor, which stood at the crossroads of all the major routes linking Central Asia and Europe. Whole societies geared themselves to the commerce in precious metals. Gold and silver were hoarded in the treasuries of temples. Copper was stored in the form of ingots, before being made into bronze weaponry by royal armourers. Often, an entire quarter of a city would be given over to such activity.

And beyond the city-states, whole empires were founded on bronze: Sumer, Egypt, and Minoan and Mycenaean Crete. These early states owed their power and influence to their arsenals of bronze.

Bronze spread quickly, but it did not appear everywhere simultaneously. It was in widespread use in the Near East at the end of the 3rd millennium BC, but it did not reach central Europe until the start of the 2nd millennium. The use of bronze was first documented in India at the end of the 3rd millennium BC, and copper was being mined in Malaysia at around the same time. In China, the appearance of tin-based bronze is roughly contemporaneous with the rise of the Shang Dynasty in around 1750 BC.

In South America, bronze artefacts first began to replace copper ones in the region around the tin deposits near Lake Titicaca. It then spread throughout the High Andes and along the Pacific coast from AD 1000 onwards.

Greek god
This bronze statue of Apollo was found in the Peloponnese. It was made using the lost-wax method in the 6th century BC.

THE LOST-WAX METHOD

Pouring molten metal into a terracotta or stone mould is all very well for making everyday objects when people are not particularly concerned about the object's final appearance. But to get a really immaculate, intricately detailed finish on a cast object, craftsmen devised the lost-wax process.

First, an accurate model of the item (the maquette) is made in wax. This is placed in a receptacle and covered with a thick layer of clay, which is left to harden and then fired. During the firing, the wax melts and runs out, leaving behind a hollow mould. Molten bronze is then poured into the mould, taking on the shape of the original wax model. Finally, when everything has cooled, the hardened clay is broken away to reveal the metal casting. Lost-wax castings made in the 15th–17th centuries by the Ife people of the Kingdom of Benin in West Africa are especially renowned.

THE EMPEROR AND THE ARTIST

One day, a Roman metalworker proudly presented a cup made from an unknown metal – in all likelihood aluminium – to Emperor Tiberius. To demonstrate the material's amazing properties, the craftsman dashed the cup to the ground, denting it badly. He then produced a small hammer and swiftly knocked out all the dents until the cup was as good as new. Tiberius was astonished, but then had the unfortunate man dragged away and beheaded and his studio razed to the ground. The Emperor feared that the new wonder metal would devalue his fortune in silver and gold. It would take almost 2,000 years, until the mid-19th century, for the secret of aluminium to be rediscovered.

Shang Dynasty bronze
A Chinese cooking pot from the 14th century BC.

Bronze as an art form

When bronze is polished, it shines almost like gold and the metal's aesthetic appeal inspired many ancient artists to work with it. By around 3000 BC, Sumerian craftsmen were hammering bronze into fine bowls, goblets and pots. The full potential of bronze as an art form became apparent with the lost-wax method, which was first developed at around the same time in Mesopotamia to make exquisitely detailed small decorative artefacts.

The Greeks and Romans took bronze sculpture to soaring new heights in the 1st millennium BC. Stylised castings of animals dating from the 8th century BC have been found at Olympia, Sparta and Corinth. Ancient depictions of the human body in bronze by notable Greek sculptors, such as Myron, Praxiteles and Phidias, often took the form of monumental statues of the gods.

The Romans produced a huge variety of bronze objects, including weapons, busts and statues. By the Middle Ages, a number of important bronze-casting centres had emerged in Europe, such as Dinant in the valley of the River Meuse. Later, during the Renaissance, bronze really came into its own as sculptors such as Benvenuto Cellini sought to emulate and surpass the art of ancient Greece and Rome.

From the blacksmiths of Sumer to the works of contemporary sculptors, bronze has never faded from the art scene. Moreover, the new working and casting methods that it generated had a profound influence on artists working in precious metals such as gold and silver.

Leaps and bounds
Sculpture developed rapidly with the invention of bronze casting, which enable artists to create extraordinary pieces like this jumping horse with boy rider. A sculpture like this one, forged in Greece in the 2nd century BC, would have been virtually impossible to make in terracotta.

An ancient profession

War may be defined as an armed conflict resulting from hostility between two social groups. It is impossible to pinpoint its first occurrence, although it is generally reckoned to have become more prevalent from around the 9th millennium BC. As people began to adopt a settled way of life, they took measures to defend what was theirs and stop others taking it from them.

Desert warfare
One section of the rock paintings at Tassili-n-Ajjer in southeastern Algeria (background) shows a battle between archers, indicating that war was already a fact of life in the Sahara c4000 BC.

Excavations of several fortified Neolithic villages have not only turned up weapons made of stone or polished flint used for hunting or warfare, they have also thrown light on how these communities lived. For example, the presence of human remains amongst food waste in the charred ruins of ancient 'fortresses' in Languedoc, southern France, point to the practice of ritual cannibalism. In addition, graves at the same site indicate certain warriors to be a class apart, occupying a superior position in the social hierarchy – as was also the case later in India and in Sparta in ancient Greece.

Arms and the man

It seems likely that the unification of Upper and Lower Egypt, which took place in around 3200 BC, could not have happened except by force of arms. In the same period, Mesopotamia was divided into around 30 city-states, whose rival claims to regional supremacy were the source of almost permanent conflict. The 'Standard of Ur', an artefact from c2600 BC discovered in the royal tombs at this Sumerian city and now housed in the British Museum, provides one of the earliest depictions of warfare. One panel shows heavy, four-wheeled war chariots, drawn by onagers or asses and ridden by chieftains, advancing ahead of foot-soldiers wearing helmets and carrying large shields. Likewise, the 'Vautours stela' from 2450 BC (now in the Louvre) shows troops from Lagash wielding lances, hatchets, scimitars and maces to triumph over the rival city-state of Umma. Grave goods from tombs at Meir indicate that by the time of the Middle Kingdom (2040–1640 BC), the Egyptian army comprised heavy infantry armed with shields and short, copper-pointed spears and light infantry equipped with bows firing bone or stone-tipped arrows.

The art of war

The role of infantry was combat at close quarters, while chariots, which were difficult to manoeuvre and carried a driver and an armed warrior, were used to attack the enemy at longer range. Chariot riders were first equipped with javelins and later with composite bows, which had far greater firepower than hunting bows. At different periods, depending on the region, warfare was transformed by the the horse and lighter, spoke-wheeled chariots. The horse introduced a whole new mode of fighting, where speed was easily as important as weight of numbers. Thus it was that the Hyksos, excellent horsemen originally from Mesopotamia, were

SOLDIERS OF FORTUNE

Mercenaries were found throughout the ancient Far East, notably in China, while the pharaohs of both Old and Middle Kingdom Egypt used Libyan and Nubian archers and Hittite cavalry. The Greeks rarely deployed mercenaries, but the armies of Rome were a kaleidoscope of fighting men from 'barbarian' cultures; the Germans (whom the Romans never fully subdued) were especially renowned for their martial skills.

SIEGE TECHNOLOGY

Besieging and capturing fortified towns called for a range of new tactics and equipment: ladders and grappling hooks were needed to scale battlements, while sapping skills were developed to undermine walls. To counter such threats, fortifications were made ever more massive, such as those that can still

Mighty walls *By the 1st millennium BC major cities such as Nineveh had erected massive defences.*

be seen at the Greek city of Mycenae or at Inca hill forts in Peru. Attackers would often use battering rams sheathed with iron or bronze to smash down gates. In around the 4th century BC, the Greeks invented the first missile-throwing siege engines, which could hurl enormous arrows or boulders weighing up to 100 kg over walls. Subsequently, ballistas and catapults were developed with even longer ranges.

able to overrun Egypt in 1630 BC and occupy it for two centuries. The horse was ideally suited to the wars of conquest later conducted by the nomads of the Central Asian steppes. Before long, all major city-states were using light chariots carrying archers. In centralised hierarchical societies, such as the Hittite Empire of Anatolia, the war-chariot was the preserve of an aristocratic warrior elite. In 1285 BC, at the Battle of Kadesh, a coalition of forces under the Hittite ruler Muwatalli II assembled almost 3,500 chariots against the armies of the Egyptian pharaoh Rameses II.

Balance of power

Most states became adept at manufacturing in quantity the hardware of warfare such as shields, breastplates, helmets and light swords. As a result, military power became less about sheer force of arms and more to do with how effectively those arms were deployed. Scientific warfare, as we now understand it, first evolved in China during the last five centuries BC. The Chinese were the first to use explosive projectiles, including grenades filled with chemical agents (such as lime, arsenic and lead oxides), in the 4th century BC.

Proud warrior
The pose struck by this magnificent bronze horseman from the Chinese Han Dynasty conveys the aura of fear and respect that surrounded men at arms in ancient societies.

On the march
Even as early as 2600 BC, armies were well-organised units, as shown on the famous Standard of Ur (left). The Sumerian chariots advance, trampling the enemy underfoot.

Regulating trade and commerce

With the invention and spread of metalworking came a new measuring instrument: scales. In enabling people to determine exactly how much of a particular commodity had been produced, or how much was available to be offered for trade, scales played a key role in the huge growth in commerce that took place around this time. The systems of weights and measures that emerged varied widely between different regions and countries, and it would be many years, in some cases millennia, before standard weights and measures were agreed.

Crafted with care
Two haematite weights from Mesopotamia, made in the shape of small creatures, c2000 BC.

Long before currency made its first appearance, in Lydia in Asia Minor in the 7th century BC, people obtained goods by barter and exchange. Yet commercial relations could only really flourish if the transaction was shown to be equitable. There had to be, therefore, a way of precisely quantifying the goods being offered for exchange. For example, a person might wish to trade a specific number of head of cattle, which were easy to count, for a specified quantity of grain. This latter commodity could either be measured by how much space it took up in a given receptacle – or by weight. Once certain metals that were heavy for their volume gained widespread acceptance as benchmarks for trade, the use of weights caught on. Hand-in-hand with weights came scales – and they were most likely invented by the peoples who, since late antiquity, had been trading throughout the Near East, from the Mediterranean coast to Asia Minor and the Persian Gulf.

Scales of eternal justice
A painted panel from a casket made in Middle Kingdom Egypt shows the jackal-headed deity Anubis using scales to weigh dead people's souls.

In the balance
Egyptian wooden scales, c1500 BC, found at Deir el-Medina in the tomb of the 18th-Dynasty architect Kha.

At each end of the beam, at an equal distance from the midpoint, were hung two identical open pans. One of these held the object to be weighed, while the other contained sufficient weights to bring the beam back to horizontal. The weight of the object was determined by totalling up the number of weights it took to achieve this. The instrument's precision depended entirely on checking that the cord was vertical and the beam in balance.

From the Romans to Roberval

By the 1st century BC the Romans were using scales with an asymmetrical beam, commonly known as the steelyard balance, which had been invented independently by the Chinese sometime in the 1st millennium BC. The principle behind such scales is simple: the balance beam is suspended from a pivot close to one end of the beam, dividing the beam into two unequal arms. The shorter arm holds the object to be weighed, which may be placed on

Position of authority
A Hittite legal functionary immortalised in stone on a funerary stela of c1000 BC (left). He holds a set of scales, emblem of his office.

Precision balance
A Gallo-Roman steelyard balance from the 1st century BC (below). The instrument used the lever principle to weigh objects without the need for separate weights. It would still be in use two millennia later.

Closely guarded standards

Scales appeared at roughly the same time in both Egypt and Mesopotamia, in the early 3rd millennium BC. The first known portrayal of a set of scales is on murals in the step-pyramid at Saqqara (2630 BC). A huge range of weights – in stone, terracotta and bronze – in various shapes and sizes has been found at sites of both these civilisations. Sumerian standard weights were based on the *shekel* (equal to 8.36 grams) and the *mina*, 60 times as heavy. Standard units of measurement of length and volume were guarded closely by ancient peoples. They were placed for safekeeping in temples and subjected to regular rigorous checks. The reliability of all transactions, both within the city-state and beyond, depended upon them.

Basic commodities, such as cereals or rice, were measured by pouring them into a receptacle marked with lines indicating quantity, or even just into a person's cupped hands. But in the case of medicinal powders, or gold or silver, there was clearly no room for such approximation. The more valuable the goods, the more stringent the regulation and the more accurate the measurement.

A question of balance

The earliest scales consisted of a beam – a horizontal rod – suspended at its midpoint from a thin, vertical cord, which was fastened to an immovable external element like a pillar.

THE LEVER

The principal of the weighing scale is based on a still more ancient invention, the lever – a rigid bar pivoting around a fulcrum that, by multiplying mechanical force, makes lifting heavy objects far easier. The Greek engineer Archimedes (287–212 BC) was one of the first people to work out the theory of the lever. He is credited with the dictum: 'Give me a place to stand and with a lever I will lift the whole world.' In his work *On the Equilibrium of Planes*, Archimedes formulated several laws explaining the principles of the way a balance works. Two of these laws were: 'Weights in equilibrium at equal distances are the same' (the classic symmetrical beam scale); and 'Magnitudes are in equilibrium at distances reciprocally proportional to their weights' (the steelyard).

a pan or hung from a hook. Via a series of notches, a counterweight slides along the longer part of the beam, effectively acting as one arm of a lever. The heavier the object, the further along the beam the counterweight must be to balance it.

Over the centuries, the accuracy and ease of use of scales was gradually improved. In the late 15th century Leonardo da Vinci is credited with devising the first scales with a graduated indicating scale, which showed the weight of the object without having to counterbalance it. In the 17th century French mathematician Gilles Personne de Roberval created the first true precision balance.

THE CALENDAR – c2800 BC
Counting time

H ow did civilisations around the world come to adopt the Gregorian calendar, the almost universal modern yardstick for counting the passage of days, months and years? The long and often complex history of the calendar reveals that early humans used natural phenomena to calculate time. The first complete calendar, devised by the Egyptians in about 4200 BC, was based on the lunar cycle.

Prehistoric observatory
Stonehenge, on Salisbury Plain in Wiltshire, is thought to have been a solar observatory and religious site.

The difference between night and day, the annual round of the seasons and their accompanying changes in weather, the regular reappearance of star patterns in the night sky were not only sources of awe and wonder to our ancient ancestors, but also of learning. By the patient observation and recording of such natural cycles, people amassed knowledge that proved invaluable, making it possible to predict natural occurrences, such as the onset of spring heralding the start of the farming year.

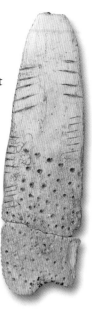

The Goseck Circle in the German province of Saxony-Anhalt, dating from the 6th millennium BC, is thought to be one of the earliest physical calendars in the world. Discovered in 2003, this Neolithic site comprises a series of concentric ditches that would once have been encircled by wooden palisades with several gates. To an observer standing in the centre of the circle, two of these gates – to the southeast and southwest – line up respectively with the position of the rising and setting Sun on the winter solstice, an event that even then could be pinpointed precisely. Later Bronze Age megaliths, such as Stonehenge in southern England and Carnac in Brittany, almost certainly functioned as calendars as well, with their various elements arranged to reveal the positions of the Sun and Moon in relation to the Earth at any given time of year.

Sumerian calculations

The Sumerians regarded the observation of celestial and climatic phenomena in much the same vein as the art of foretelling the future, for example by haruspicy – reading the entrails of sacrificed animals for omens. Yet the vast astronomical knowledge

Marking time
Human beings have always felt the fundamental urge to mark the passage of time and this piece of notched reindeer bone is an early example (far left). It was found at Eyzies in the Dordogne region of France and dates from c25,000 BC. The pictograms (left) are less ancient, being part of a Neolithic astrological table from Mesopotamia.

A BRIEF HISTORY OF EARLY TIMEPIECES

The oldest instrument for measuring time was the gnomon, a simple stick set upright in the ground. People noted the changing length of its shadow as the sun passed overhead. The gnomon was the precursor of the sundial, which appeared in Egypt in *c*1500 BC. It was divided into 12 hours, from the rising to the setting of the sun, but the length of the hours, just like that of the days, varied according to the seasons. Another ancient timepiece was the clepsydra, or water clock, invented by the Egyptians in the 16th century BC. This was a vessel with a hole in its base that was filled with

water. As the water trickled out, the level inside the vessel dropped at a steady rate and the time could be read off against a series of marks. The incense clock was a popular device in China invented in the 6th century BC. It was used to measure fairly short periods – from minutes to hours or days – by the time it took for incense of a known combustion rate to burn down.

In the 8th century AD, the first mechanical clock appeared signalling a radical new departure: this measured time not by the passage of the Sun or some physical action like water flow, but by the mechanical movement of cogwheels activated at regular intervals by a falling weight. These very early clocks had no face or hands, they simply marked each passing hour. The first pendulum clock was built by the Dutch astronomer Christiaan Huygens in 1657, based on Galileo's observations on the motion of pendulums. It could measure time far more accurately than any previous device.

Water clock
An illumination of a clepsydra from a 13th-century Islamic manuscript.

they collected – they were able, for instance, to predict lunar eclipses, solstices and equinoxes – enabled them to draw up the first lunar calendar early in the 3rd millennium BC. Noting that the Moon took 29 or 30 days, depending on the time of year, to complete its phase cycle (to be precise, 29.53 days), they divided the year into 12 lunar months, six with 29 and six with 30 days, making a total of 354 days in the year.

To make up for the discrepancy between this and the solar year, which had 365 days, they inserted a 13th month. Exactly when this short extra month fell was determined quite arbitrarily by the individual rulers of city-states. It was often timed to coincide with tax payments or a ceremonial offering to the gods. Since this method of correcting the calendar was very much ad hoc, it was not uncommon for harvesting to begin well after the month actually named for the activity.

The Mesopotamian calendar

For everyday purposes, the inhabitants of the city-states of Mesopotamia dispensed with the official calendar in favour of a simplified, or 'schematic', one which was based on the 360-day calendar count that merchants used to conduct business. It was only in the second half of the 1st millennium BC that Babylonian royal astronomers came to calculate the positions of the Moon and Sun, paying special attention to the distance between these two celestial bodies and the horizon. Their observations showed that 235 lunar months (measured from the first appearance of the new moon) were equivalent to 19 solar years (measured according to observation of the summer solstice). From this they devised a

lunisolar calendar, which factored in an intercalary, or 'leap' month, to bring the lunar months and solar year in line with one another.

Egyptian timekeeping

The Egyptians traditionally used a lunar calendar, but this proved unsuitable for their farming needs, in particular for calculating the best times for sowing crops. During the reign of Pharaoh Djoser, in around 2700 BC, the

Written in the stars
Animal figures symbolising various constellations are depicted on this fresco from the tomb of Seti I, who was buried in the Valley of the Kings in the 13th century BC. In ancient times astronomy was synonymous with astrology.

lunar calendar was replaced by one comprising 12 months of 30 days each, almost certainly based on the Mesopotamian schematic calendar. Priests continued to use the lunar calendar to set the dates of religious festivals.

In the new Egyptian calendar, each month was divided into three periods of 10 days known as the 'decans'. In turn, the 12 months were arranged into three groups of four months each, and these corresponded to the three agricultural periods, known as Akhet (flood), Peret (growth or germination), and Chemou (harvest). Outside this scheme, five further days – which the Greeks called *epagomenes* (literally, 'those that are above') – were added to make a year of 365 days.

A heaven-sent star

The ancient Egyptian year began on the 1st of Thoth (July 19 in the Gregorian calendar). This was the day on which the star they called Sothis – Sirius, the Dog-Star, the brightest star in the sky – reappeared after a 70-day period of occultation. The star appears just before sunrise and the Egyptians associated it with their goddess Isis, wife of Osiris. As such, it was held in great reverence and its reappearance was celebrated with lavish festivals.

The schematic civil calendar of ancient Egypt consisted of 365 days, whereas a 'real' (or 'sidereal') year – that is, the time it takes for the Earth to go around the Sun – is slightly longer, at approximately 365 and a quarter days. Over time – and the civilisation of ancient Egypt lasted a very long time – all of these additional quarter days added up to push the civil year out of kilter with the seasons,

earning it the name of 'vague year'. In many ways this did not really matter. Over an average person's lifetime the discrepancy amounted to just about a fortnight, while in regulating their daily working lives, Egyptian farmers paid little heed to the civil calendar. But the religious authorities found the discrepancy a nuisance, since ceremonies linked to the seasons gradually moved further from their appropriate time – the harvest festival, for example, ended up being held in mid-winter. Accordingly, in 238 BC, Pharaoh Ptolemy III Euergetes issued the Decree of Canopus, which introduced a sixth extra epagomenal day every 4 years. He might have expected the clergy to be grateful, but the reform met with resistance, especially from the priests, and was never instituted in practice.

The calendar goes global

The Greeks inherited the Babylonian lunisolar calendar of 12 months of 30 days each, but because it was not geared to the seasons, people preferred to use calendars known as parapegms that linked seasonal tasks to astronomical events. These parapegms coexisted alongside official calendars, which were hampered by the mismatch between solar and lunar months. Eventually, a calendar of 354 days was devised, alternating 30-day 'full' months with 29-day 'hollow' months, to which was later added (during the time of the statesman Solon in Athens, *c*600 BC) an intercalary month of 30 days every two years. This was referred to as an 'embolismic month'. In Athens it was inserted after the sixth month of the year, which was called Poseidon, but elsewhere it was generally placed at the end of the year. But the system was inherently flawed, in that it created a year of 369 days – too long compared with the solar year.

Caesar's reforms

For much of its history, the Roman Republic used a lunar calendar. The year comprised 355 days divided into 12 months of varying length. This left the calendar just over 10 days short of the solar year, so intercalary months were occasionally added to keep the calendar in line with the seasons. By the time of Julius Caesar, the calendar had become hopelessly confused, so, in consultation with the mathematician Sosigenes of Alexandria, he instituted a major calendar reform in 46 BC.

In the new system, the 12 months of the year all had 30 or 31 days except for February, the shortest month with 28 days. Every fourth

THE MAYAN CALENDAR – A REMARKABLE FEAT OF CALCULATION

In the 1st century AD, the Maya of Central America managed to establish the length of the year with even greater accuracy than the Gregorian calendar some 15 centuries later. The Mayan solar calendar (*Haab*) comprised 360 days (18 months of 20 days each) plus five hollow or 'nameless' days at the end of the year. This 'everyday' calendar was used as an agricultural measure to mark the changing of the seasons.

The Maya used various units to measure time: a period of 20 days was called a *uinal*; 18 uinals made a *tun*; and 20 *tuns* made a *katun*. The *katun* (totalling 7,200 days, or 20 years) was the basic unit of the so-called Long Count Calendar, which counted a 5,125-year cycle and could be used to identify any day by counting the number of days passed since August 11, 3114 BC, when Mayan civilisation was believed to have begun. The Maya also worked out a precise table showing the phases and eclipses of the Moon, solar eclipses and the transit of Venus. Relying entirely on the naked eye, they had calculated the movement of the planet Venus to within a margin of error of just 2 hours over a period of 500 years.

The Mayan ability to perform extraordinary calculations derived from their mastery of advanced mathematics. By the early years BC, they were already familiar with a positional notation system and the concept of zero (the latter was not known in western Europe until about AD 1200, coming via the Arabs, who had themselves learned it from India). But perhaps the most surprising facet of the Mayan conception of time was the very modern distinction they drew between linear time – encompassing the past, present and future – and human time, which is characterised by its cyclical nature. The French historian Jacques Soustelle went so far as to state that the Maya were 'possibly the only people on Earth ever to have worshipped time'.

Mayan manuscript *The 11th-century Dresden Codex (below) contains remarkably accurate astronomical tables.*

Aztec disc *Short-count calendars based on the Mayan calendar were used throughout ancient Mesoamerica to mark the sacred year. This elaborately carved stone sun-disc is an example from the Aztec culture of the 15th-16th centuries.*

High days and telling time

A fragment of a Roman calendar (top) lists religious fast days known as the Amiternines. To tell the time, the Egyptians used both the sundial (above centre) and the gnomon (above).

year an extra day was to be added to February to make the year 366 days long, rather than the usual 365. This was done by repeating February 23 (there was no 29). Since February 23 was, according to the Roman dating system, the sixth day before the calends (first day) of March, its new twin day became designated as the 'second sixth day before the calends of March', in Latin *bis sextus ante calendas martias*, which is still recalled in the term 'bissextile' to refer to leap years.

It was further determined that the vernal or spring equinox (when day and night are of equal length) should fall on March 25 every year. To do this, the year when the reform took place – 708 AUC (from *ab urbe condita*, the 'founding of the city'), or 46 BC in modern terms – was lengthened by 90 days. Finally, the beginning of the year was fixed as January 1, rather than March 1.

The Julian Calendar remained in use for more than 1,500 years, but eventually it, too, registered

DAYS OF THE WEEK

The ancient Roman calendar followed a primitive system for naming the days, with certain days used as markera – the Calends (first day of the month), the Nones (fifth day), and the Ides (13th day). This system was later replaced by the seven-day week, borrowed from the Hebrews. The days of the week were named after the Sun (*Dies Solis*, Sunday), the Moon (*Dies Lunae*, Monday) and the planets that were known about at the time – Mars (*Dies Martis*, Tuesday), Mercury (*Dies Mercurii*, Wednesday), Jupiter (*Dies Jovis*, Thursday), Venus (*Dies Veneris, Friday),* and Saturn (*Dies Saturni*, Saturday).

Calendrical craft
A silver-gilt perpetual calendar made by an 18th-century German silversmith, Johann Martin.

Reading runes

An almanac from Norway, made up of 10 thin wooden panels engraved with runic symbols.

a discrepancy of several days from the solar (or 'tropical') year. The solar year is precisely 365.2422 days long, whereas the Julian year lasted on average 365.25 days. This computed to a 1-day shortfall every 128 years, or about 3 days for every 400 years that passed.

Enter Gregory XIII

In 1582, in the course of deliberations over the date on which Easter should fall that year, it emerged that the Julian Calendar was 10 days behind the tropical year. Ever since the First Council of Nicaea in AD 325, Easter had been celebrated on the first Sunday following the full moon after the vernal equinox (March 21); on no account could Easter fall before March 22 or after April 25. But in 1582, the vernal equinox took place on March 11, according to the calendar, rather than March 21.

To correct the discrepancy, Pope Gregory XIII proposed that the Church adopt a new calendar to be named after him. To bring the vernal equinox back to March 21, where it had been in the year 325, ten days had to be lost from the Julian Calendar – in 1582 the entire Catholic world would jump directly from October 4 to October 15. Gregory further decreed that the number of leap years in every 400 years would be reduced from 100 to 97: all years divisible by 100 reverted to being regular years of 365 days (except those divisible by 400, which remained leap years).

Spread of the Gregorian Calendar

At first, only Roman Catholic countries adopted Gregory's new calendar. Spain and Portugal instituted it at the same time as Rome, while France modified its system later in the same year, when December 9 was immediately followed by December 20. Poland adopted the calendar in 1586, and Hungary followed suit the next year. Protestant England and Sweden did not switch until 1752 and 1753 respectively, by which time they had to lose 11 days. Orthodox Christian countries stuck with the Julian Calendar until the early 20th century, but eventually came into line with the rest of the world. The decision might have been influenced by the fate of the Russian athletes in the 1908 Olympic Games staged in London – having arranged their schedule according to the Julian Calendar, they arrived after the games had already ended. The Soviet Union switched in 1918, which moved the date of the Revolution from October 24-25, 1917, to November 6-7. Greece followed suit in 1923, losing 13 days, and Turkey in 1926.

Astronomical table

An illuminated page from a medieval ephemeris – a document giving the positions of celestial bodies. Such tables, which are still calculated today, were first produced in the 4th century BC.

The first polymath

It is one of history's ironies that the name of the royal architect Imhotep is now better known than that of his patron, Pharaoh Djoser, the founder of ancient Egypt's Third Dynasty. Acting on Djoser's instructions, in around 2630 BC Imhotep built the Saqqara step-pyramid, one of the oldest surviving funerary monuments in the world.

Imhotep's lasting fame derives from the fact that, like Aristotle and Leonardo da Vinci after him, he epitomises the polymath who had his finger on the pulse of all contemporary branches of learning. We know virtually nothing about him as a person, other than that he was the son of an architect from near Memphis on the Nile. What we do know is that he pushed back the frontiers of knowledge in his time and opened up new horizons

The Old Kingdom

Archaeological evidence enables us to reconstruct a fairly accurate picture of Old Kingdom Egypt, including how much was known about various technologies. The life of the country, which was unified under Pharaonic rule in 3150 BC, was governed by the annual Nile flood, which set the parameters for all agricultural activity. Despite the fact that people had mastered irrigation techniques by this stage, farming methods remained fairly crude. Copper was widely used for tools, though not yet bronze, and the Egyptians were unfamiliar with both the wheel and the lever. The art of stonemasonry was practised, but all buildings, from domestic dwellings to temples and monuments, were still made of mud bricks. And while medicine was beginning to adopt the principles of empirical observation and rationality, it still remained rooted in superstition and magic.

A man of many parts

An inscription on the plinth of a statue at Saqqara lists Imhotep's many titles: 'Chancellor of the king of Lower Egypt, first in line after the king, administrator of the great palace, hereditary nobleman, High Priest of Heliopolis … builder and chief sculptor'. He also amassed a succession of political posts that made him the second most important person in Egypt after the Pharaoh and he took on various priestly roles, thereby acquiring a religious power base. In addition – an extraordinary achievement for a commoner – he was granted the right to perform certain highly specialised tasks. He is traditionally believed to have been an agronomist and to have written a work on ethics. Furthermore, no doubt in his capacity as chief priest, he is thought to have been an astronomer.

In an age when religion was still the source of all secular authority, Imhotep freed himself from the traditional role of the doctor-priest, whom the gods granted the power to cure the sick, supplanting it with that of the medical practitioner applying methods founded on observation and reason. Some specialists regard him as the inspiration behind many key passages in the Ebers Papyrus, the most important medical text of ancient Egypt, written in *c*1550 BC, which outlines the rudiments of anatomy, describes a number of illnesses and their treatment, and provides the formulae for various drugs.

The first pyramid

Imhotep's main claim to fame is as the designer and architect of Egypt's first pyramid, built as a vast mortuary complex for Pharaoh Djoser. The pyramid is situated at Saqqara on the left (west) bank of the Nile, just north of the city of Memphis, on the border between Lower and Upper Egypt. The design builds on the *mastaba*, a flat-roofed rectangular tomb with sloping sides, set within a high-walled enclosure that also housed several temples and chapels. We have no idea what inspired Imhotep, but in his hands the *mastaba*, which originally reached a height of 8 metres, became the core of the pyramid. He created a massive

FROM MAN TO GOD

Some 2,000 years after his death, Imhotep was revered throughout Egypt as a god of medicine and healing and as the son of the deity Ptah. Many temples were dedicated to him, and his cult remained popular right up to the conquest of Egypt by Alexander the Great in 331 BC. The ancient Greeks called him 'Imoutes' and came to identify him with Asclepius, their own god of healing.

structure that rose from this rectangular base through six rectangular terraces of descending size to reach a height of 62 metres.

The monument is first and foremost a political statement expressing the power of the Pharaoh in life and in death – its stepped shape resembles a staircase ascending to heaven, symbolising the Pharaoh's ascent on his death. It is also an architectural masterpiece. One major innovation was that it was built not of mud bricks, but of stone – polished white limestone, which was relatively easy to cut. Moreover, the blocks of stone were fitted carefully together, with their edges bevelled, to ensure maximum stability for the structure. At Saqqara, Imhotep created the first mortuary complex entirely composed of quarried stone. As the progenitor of the pyramids that have exerted such a powerful fascination on mankind, Imhotep may be regarded as the ultimate ancestor of all architects.

Memorials to genius
Long after his death, Imhotep continued to be revered by the ancient Egyptians. The votive statue opposite (far left) was made more than 2,000 years after he built the famous step-pyramid of Djoser (background). The plinth below, dating from the time of the Old Kingdom, shows Imhotep's name inscribed in hieroglyphs.

Healing through harmony

Now practised widely in the West, acupuncture had its origins in Bronze Age China. In common with all other forms of Chinese medicine, it forms part of a holistic conception of a harmonious relationship between the body and the external world.

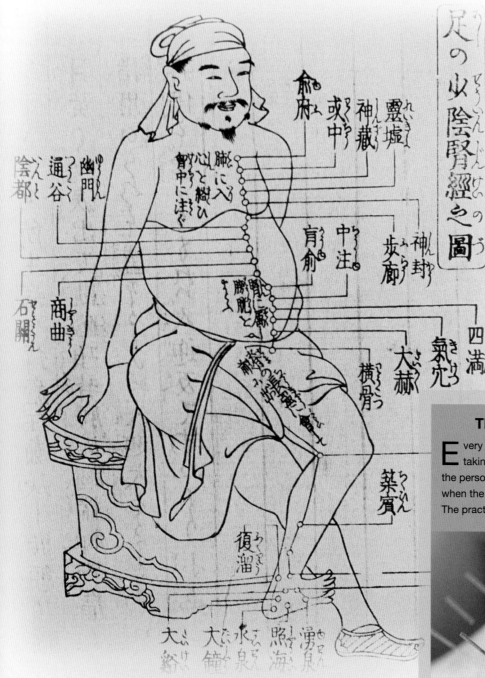

Although the term 'acupuncture' is quite recent – it was coined by Jesuit missionaries in the 17th century – the practice it refers to is ancient. According to Chinese tradition, it was invented by the legendary ruler Huangdi in around 2600 BC. In fact, the discovery of this healing technique, which involves stimulating points of the body with fine needles, probably owes much to chance and experiment. Perhaps after accidentally pricking themselves, someone found that it relieved an ache or pain. Encouraged to try to repeat the effect, they could gradually have located the point where it was most effective and then identified what the precise effect was in each case.

The earliest known acupuncture needles are made from sharpened flint and date from the mid-4th millennium BC. Later, needles of bone, bamboo and even terracotta were used, before copper, iron and gold needles became widespread in the first century BC. Today, most acupuncture needles are stainless steel.

Yin and *Yang* – universal duality

Acupuncture is based on the quintessential Chinese concept that there are two opposing forces in every phenomenon: an active, male principle (*yang*) and a passive, female principle (*yin*). The two are represented visually by the *taiji*, a circle in which a white *yang* element rises on the left and interlocks with a black *yin* element descending on the right. This duality determines all the rhythms that exist in the world, including the human body.

THE PULSE – A VITAL INDICATOR

Every acupuncture session begins with the practitioner taking the patient's pulse. From this the physician can feel the person's rising and falling *yang*, and so pinpoint the moment when the rhythm is disrupted, which is what causes the illness. The practitioner can also determine whether the disturbance is the result of an excess or deficiency of *yang*, either of which upset the fine balance between *yin* and *yang*.

Medical theory and practice
A diagram of acupuncture points on the body indicates which points relate to which ailments (far left). Left: acupuncture needles inserted into a patient.

In this scheme of things, an illness is seen as a disruption of the harmony between a person and the cosmos – an imbalance between a person's internal rhythm and that of the world around. Inserting and manipulating needles into precise points along the body's meridians restores equilibrium by releasing blockages and regulating the flow of energy.

An ancient remedy in modern use

Acupuncture was introduced into Japan in the 5th century AD. It became known in the West in the 16th century, from the accounts of travellers and missionaries, but it was not until the 19th century that a few Western doctors began practising it. Its first recorded use was by Dr L V J Berlioz (father of the composer) who treated a woman with abdominal pain at the Paris medical school in 1810. The first British practitioner was the surgeon John Churchill, who in 1821 published his results on the treatment of tympany (a chest condition) and rheumatism. Its use has extended to anaesthesia, making surgery possible with the patient still conscious. It works by sending tiny electrical charges through needles, which inhibit the transmission of pain sensation to the brain.

ANCIENT TEXTS

The basic principles behind traditional acupuncture were elucidated in the *Nei Jing*, a medical treatise whose author and date are unknown, but which certainly predates the Christian era. The first work to refer specifically to acupuncture and to the use of moxa – small sticks of *Artemisia* that are ignited to heat the skin at particular acupuncture points – is the *Zhen Jiu Jia Yi King*. This was the work of the scholar Huangfu Mi (AD 215–282), who was responsible for identifying the 649 acupuncture points on the human body and for naming 349 of them.

Man and the cosmos

According to Chinese belief, the vital energy known as *qi* or *chi* flows through every living organism in a regular rhythm. The energy flow follows 14 pathways known as meridians. Twelve of these are the main meridians arranged symmetrically on left and right sides of the organism, while two stand alone on the midline of the front and back of the head and trunk. Each meridian corresponds to an organ or a function and carries acupuncture points linked to that particular organ, so 11 points relate to the lungs, 45 to the stomach and 47 to the bladder. There are 649 in total.

LEARNING THE TRADE

Unlike many countries, where medical knowledge was the preserve of a few, in China the practice of acupuncture became the subject of a standardised educational programme. Aspiring acupuncturists learned with the help of a mannequin marked with meridians and acupuncture points. The earliest of these instructional models were made in the 11th century, in the Song Dynasty. The candidate would be tested on a mannequin filled with water on which all the acupuncture points were invisibly plugged with wax. The water would trickle out of points pricked by the candidate, showing incontrovertibly if they were right or wrong.

Scale model *An acupuncture mannequin from the 18th century.*

From magic to medical treatment

O ne overriding and abiding concern for early humans was how to alleviate pain and treat injuries. The first forms of treatment were rudimentary and rooted in superstition, but they were also, at least in part, based on observation and experience. In this respect, these folk remedies prefigured the rational medicine developed by the ancient Greeks.

In 1996, near the village of Ensisheim in Alsace, a team of archaeologists excavating a Neolithic burial site unearthed a human skull bearing the marks of two incidents of trepanning – a surgical procedure in which holes are bored into the skull. They dated the skull to around 7000 BC. This distant human ancestor – the first medical patient we know of to date – clearly demonstrated that people knew how to carry out quite complex medical procedures. Although there was nothing to indicate that the second operation had been successful, it did prove that the first had been done competently enough to enable a man whose cranium had been drilled into to survive at least for a while.

Excavations at this and several other widely dispersed sites from China to Mesoamerica have provided archaeologists with a fairly accurate picture of the state of medical knowledge in the Neolithic. In addition to performing trepanations, early *Homo sapiens* knew how to set broken bones, amputate limbs and cauterise wounds. They were also well versed in the medicinal properties of plants.

The realm of magic

The early forms of medical treatment, which varied from one region to another, did have an empirical basis, but medicine in general was still dominated by religious belief which commonly regarded illnesses or accidents as forms of divine punishment. The only way to

Gods of medicine
The Babylonian goddess of healing was Gula, shown here (left) in a relief carving from about 1300 BC. The fearsome wind-demon Pazuzu (right) was the bringer of plague and fevers, but he was also thought to drive away other evil spirits, and Babylonians kept his image as a lucky charm. Below: The seal of an Assyrian physician, Makkar-Marduk.

Materia medica
A stall in the Chinese city of Xinjiang (far right) displays traditional remedies, including dried reptile skins, roots, bark and powders made from animal organs and plants. Herbal and folk medicine is still widely used in China.

guarantee that a treatment would be effective and ensure a person's recovery was to appease the gods or spirits by intoning the requisite spells and incantations. Ancient medicine was inextricably bound up with magic, an attitude that persisted down the ages and still survives in some forms of folk remedies.

Precise prescriptions

Following the invention of a writing system in Mesopotamia in the 4th millennium BC, people began to record information on medical practice and much of this has come down to us. The largest collection of ancient prescriptions, inscribed on stone tablets, was found at the Sumerian city of Nippur. Other records, especially from the neo-Assyrian and neo-Babylonian periods (respectively the 11th–8th centuries and 7th–6th centuries BC), include correspondence between doctors, 'handbooks' for exorcists and manuals on combating particular diseases. One pre-Babylonian text is remarkably precise: 'If a man is sick with jaundice, soak liquorice root in milk and let it rest overnight under the stars before mixing it with purified oil. Then administer it to the patient and it will cure him.'

Limits of knowledge

These texts give us a good idea of how advanced ancient Mesopotamian medical knowledge was. As well as knowing how to treat various 'simple' illnesses, they could mend fractures and dislocations, and carry out some surgical procedures. Antiseptic oils were used during surgery to guard against post-operative infection. They had also identified several diseases of the eyes, but had not yet worked out how to operate on them. Perhaps most surprisingly, Mesopotamian medical texts display an awareness of mental conditions such as anxiety and depression, although it would be overstating the case to claim that this represents the birth of psychiatry

Doctors and exorcists

Much medical procedure in Mesopotamia was still in thrall to magic, but no amount of prayers to Gula, the goddess of healing (one of the few deities to retain a separate identity and not be absorbed into the chief god Ishtar), or to Ea, the god of water, could substitute for timely intervention by a competent medical practitioner. At this stage, doctors did not have their own guild: Mesopotamian healers, who were called *ashipu*, were priests who had received special training. They would first diagnose the ailment and then set about curing the patient with a mixture of prayers and

genuine medical procedures. In identifying the illness, the *ashipu* worked in close concert with a soothsayer, or *baru*.

Another type of healer, the *asu*, specialised in herbal remedies. These healers practiced medicine based on empirical knowledge were often referred to in Mesopotamian texts as 'physician'. But it would be wrong to see the *ashipu* and *asu* as polar opposites, the one dispensing magical cures and the other rational remedies, as there was a blurring of roles, with the two approaches complementing one another rather than competing. The author of a letter to the king of Mari has left us a good account of what took place at a consultation between an *asu* named Meranum and a *baru* called Ishi-Addu: 'While Ishi-Addu questioned the oracle, Meranum applied dressings.'

The healing power of plants

The training for Mesopotamian doctor-priests consisted of studying ancient treatises kept in the temples. This stress on 'book-learning'

The embalmer's art
Anubis (top), the jackal-headed god associated with the afterlife and mummification, watches over the mummy of Sennedjem, a pharaoh from the 13th century BC.

explains the highly formulaic nature of diagnoses and suggested remedies in this period. Diagnosis attempted to get to the root cause of a patient's illness by identifying and then purging the sin that had caused the symptoms. Medicines were made from a variety of plants, minerals such as salt or saltpetre (potassium nitrate) and from animal products like tortoiseshell or milk. Ground down and mixed with excipients ('carriers') such as beer, vinegar or honey, they were administered to patients in different forms, as appropriate – lotions, syrups, ointments, poultices, even suppositories.

Medicine under the pharaohs

Examination of Egyptian skeletons and mummies reveals signs of such diseases as infectious rheumatism, bilharzia (still greatly feared along the Nile), tuberculosis, hardening of the arteries and polio, and also yields evidence of surgery. And yet countless passages in manuscripts and images on the walls of temples paint a uniformly optimistic picture of pharaonic medicine. The guiding light of ancient Egyptian medicine was Imhotep, who

was deified by the Egyptians. The Greeks identified him with Aesculapius, their own god of healing. As in Mesopotamia, medicine was subservient to religion, and medical practice involved calling upon Horus and other gods to protect the physician from infection and dispel the demons afflicting the patient. Doctor-priests were initiated into the secrets of medicine in the temple schools at Memphis and Thebes (Luxor).

Map of the human body

Anatomical and physiological knowledge in ancient Egypt was based on dissections undertaken as part of the embalming process. The system of canals that spread out from the Nile to irrigate Egypt's agricultural land served as a model for the inner workings of the body. Egyptian anatomical diagrams show vessels running from the heart and extending to every part of the body. As well as oxygen, these vessels were thought to carry every type of bodily

Tools of the trade
A Roman bas-relief shows a surgeon's instruments from the 1st century AD (below). The Egyptian papyrus behind it, dating from 1325 BC, describes illnesses, symptoms and treatments.

EARLY OBSERVATIONS

Over time, observation became an integral part of Egyptian medical practice, and in all likelihood involved formal examination of patients. At least this is what one passage from the Ebers Papyrus of *c*1550 BC appears to suggest, when it states that 'the ear hears what is beneath'. The document also contains chapters on contraceptive methods and diagnosing pregnancy. As in Mesopotamia, Egyptian physicians relied on scholarly treatises recopied by temple scribes and passed down through generations. The idea that Egyptian medicine may gradually have freed itself from the hold of religion is corroborated by the roughly contemporary Edwin Smith Papyrus, which describes rational surgical procedures based on observable anatomy, with no mention of accompanying magic formulae.

ANCIENT ANTIBIOTICS

It is now known that the Chinese were using antibiotics in the treatment of wounds and infections of the skin by around 1500 BC. They used a paste made from fermented soya beans that had been left to grow a penicillin-rich mould. Likewise, the discovery of earthenware pots containing a natural form of streptomycin suggests that the ancient Egyptians knew about the antiseptic properties of this fungus at least 3,000 years ago.

fluid, including blood, semen and tears, along with foodstuffs, fecal matter and disease-causing elements known as *ukhedu*. The pulse was seen as the 'place where the heart speaks', and the function of the lungs was considered more important than that of the liver.

Over 5,000 years, the ancient Egyptians amassed so much knowledge that Egypt is generally regarded as the birthplace of modern medicine. The Egyptians had words for around a hundred diseases and ailments, including metritis (inflammation of the uterus), urinary conditions such as diabetic polyuria, many eye diseases, dysentery, intestinal parasitosis, dermatitis and tonsilitis. Their surgeons knew how to treat both simple and compound fractures. Important medical texts have survived, including those known today as the Edwin Smith (1600 BC), Ebers (1550 BC) and Brugsch (1300 BC) papyruses.

Pharmaceutical know-how

There is no doubting the ancient Egyptians' breadth of pharmaceutical knowledge. Almost 70 organic animal-based products – including such unlikely substances as crocodile blood, baboon hair, scorpion infusion and cat uterus – together with 20 or so plant species (palm, acacia, cedar, sycamore) and as many minerals (powdered lapis lazuli, arsenic sulphide, lead salt, sea salt) were used to concoct an astonishing range of unguents, potions and poultices. Doctors administered their medicines to patients after mixing them with a variety of bases, varying from beer, milk and animal fat to the milk of a woman recently gone into labour, and even, in some cases, excrement. Alongside infusions, balms, ointments and lotions, other ways of administering drugs were developed, including vaginal injections (using animal horns) and drops instilled into the eye with a vulture's feather as a cure for conjunctivitis.

The great Hippocrates

The Greek physician Hippocrates (*c*460–377 BC) is widely hailed as the father of modern medicine. His fame rests not so much on his theory of medicine – which was based on the notion that the human body was made up of the four base elements or 'humours': fire, water, earth and air – as on his contribution to

Lucky charms
The 'Eye of Horus' (below) and the amulets opposite (centre and far left) were charms designed to protect the wearer from evil spirits and sickness.

THE PRECURSOR OF ASPIRIN

Discovered in 1893 by the German chemist Heinrich Dreser, acetylsalicylic acid, a key ingredient of aspirin, is the synthetic form of a natural substance present in willow bark (hence its name, from *Salix*, the Latin name for willow). Infusions of willow bark were prescribed by doctors 2,000 years ago in ancient Greece to ease rheumatic pains and inflammation.

Consultations
A Greek vase from the 5th century AD (above) shows the practice of blood-letting, which remained part of medical treatment for centuries. The relief panel (right) shows Aesculapius, the Greek god of medicine, treating a bedridden woman.

clinical practice. It was Hippocrates who established the paramount importance of examining the patient. As heir to both the Greek natural philosophers and a native school of medicine going back to the 6th century BC, Hippocrates paved the way for the first dissections of human cadavers, conducted by Herophilos and Erasistratus in the 4th century BC. These early anatomists took their cue from Aristotle, who pioneered animal dissection.

The Greeks were also responsible for introducing medicine to Rome, where it had traditionally been regarded as a discipline fit only for slaves. The Hippocratic Oath, which is still taken today by medical students receiving their doctorates, proclaims the ethical principles of the medical profession, foremost among which is patient confidentiality.

The influence of Galen

Aside from Aulus Cornelius Celsus, who during the reign of Augustus collated the medical knowledge of the age into a major treatise, *De Medicina*, the foremost figure in Roman medicine is Galen of Pergamum (AD 131–201), a physician who was born in Greece but spent his life in Rome. Upholding the doctrine of the four humours previously expounded by Hippocrates, Galen added his own theory of four temperaments – sanguine, phlegmatic, choleric, melancholic – and confirmed the importance of observation in making diagnoses. His dissections of pigs and dogs resulted in major new insights into the nervous system and the heart, but many of Galen's ideas on anatomy were wrong, such as his assertion that the human heart had two chambers and that the liver was at the centre of the circulatory system.

With the aid of human dissections, the Flemish physician Andreas Vesalius (1514–64) eventually disproved many of Galen's theories, but throughout the centuries in between, Galen's teachings held sway in Europe's

وبرسى طلق اذردنه بواج داغكم واددُ مكواة مسمارى بله اور سنعا اولهان بَاُلَكَ

صُورَةُ طَبِيبٍ
وَشَكَلِ آلَت
وَصُورَةُ عَلِيلٍ
بُوَلِرَ دَدُ

اللَّي يَنْبَحِي نَصَ

Practitioners

The gesticulating clay figure (left) represents a Chinese sorcerer-healer from the 1st century AD; he is performing gyrations believed to ward off demons. In the 15th-century Ottoman manuscript above, a physician is shown drawing off peritoneal fluid from a patient suffering from oedema.

medical faculties. In particular, Galen's contempt for surgery effectively discredited this vital branch of medicine until it was rehabilitated by the French surgeon Ambroise Paré in the 16th century. After Galen, medicine continued to advance in the West, but slowly. The main medical trailblazers were the seats of learning in Islamic countries, notably the medical school established by Avicenna (Ibn Sina, 980–1037) in the Persian city of Isfahan.

The Chinese legacy

Prior to the 18th century, the exchange of ideas between Asia and Europe was minimal. As a result, Europe did not benefit from early medical discoveries in the Far East. The Romans and their successors, the Byzantines, persisted in believing that blood originated in the liver, even though in China it was established as early as the 2nd century BC that blood is pumped around the body by the heart. Europe would wait until 1628 before English physician William Harvey set out a new understanding of the heart and circulation of the blood. Another Chinese idea that went unrecognised by Western medicine, this time until the second half of the 20th century, was that of circadian and monthly rhythms. We now know that these rhythms play an important role in human physiology and that certain diseases, such as Hodgkin's lymphoma or duodenal ulcers, follow a course attributable to them. The concept of natural rhythms has been promoted in the practice of acupuncture, as outlined in Chinese texts, such as the *Manual on the Selection of Acupuncture Points According to the Months and Seasons.*

THE CHINESE AND HORMONES

From the 2nd century BC, the Chinese were isolating male and female sex hormones in urine and using them to treat certain illnesses. This was the early foundation of endocrinology. The hormones were later distilled and concentrated into pills, which were prescribed for the treatment of such conditions as sterility and impotence. They were administered in large doses, leading medical scholars to speculate that early Chinese physicians may have been aware that oestrogen is neutralised by the liver.

SKIS – *c*2500 BC

Travelling over snow

The incredibly simple idea of strapping pieces of bark or wooden planks to the feet in order to move around more easily on snow sparked the invention of snowshoes and skis. The term 'ski' comes from the Old Norse word 'skid', meaning a wooden board.

Crossing country
A Sami hunter on skis, in an engraving of 1673. His descendants are the modern cross-country skiers, like those pictured behind, trekking in Colorado.

The ice and snow that covers the far north of Europe and Asia for many months of the year dictated that people use some mode of sliding along in order to hunt, fish or fight effectively. In this case, necessity truly was the mother of invention, giving rise to a form of locomotion that was brilliantly efficient over the terrain.

A long history

The first things that people strapped to their feet for traction were simple animal skins. Later, they added pieces of wood to gain a

firmer footing. Little by little, the woods were lengthened for greater efficiency. Skis are pictured in ancient rock carvings discovered at Rødøy (*c*4000 BC) and Tjoetta (*c*2000 BC) in Norway, while a set of fossilised wooden skis, dating from around 2500 BC, was found preserved in a peat bog at Hoting in Sweden in 1921. All of these finds indicate that the ancestors of modern skiers habitually carried some form of stick, possibly a spear.

Early skis comprised two long, straight pieces of wood; the Hoting skis, for example, are made from strips of pine just over 1 metre in length and 20 cm wide and pointed at the tips. Other ancient skis from Sweden, Norway and Finland are up to 3 metres long. Skis made by the Lapp (Sami) people of northern Norway and Sweden were of unequal length, with the shorter one being used for propulsion and the longer one to steer. Made from durable walnut or ash, they had strips of fur or skin tacked onto their soles.

The birth of modern skiing

As a basic mode of transport in Nordic countries, the ski barely evolved from ancient designs until skiing became popular as a sport and leisure activity in the 19th century. Two major problems were solved at this time: how to ensure that the skis stayed on the feet, and how to turn easily without losing them. Both of these key innovations were the brainchild of Sondre Norheim, a native of the Telemark region

Diverse styles

As early as 1910, this leisurely cross-country skier (right) was using purpose-built skis. The modern competitor in the downhill (below) is using skis that measure 2.4 metres in length and can run at speeds close to 250km/h (150mph).

SKIING ONTO THE THRONE

In the winter of 1520, Sweden was under attack by the Danes, who were besieging Stockholm. The Swedes mounted organised resistance under the leadership of a nobleman, Gustavus Vasa. In one decisive battle, he was reinforced in the nick of time by ski-borne troops; he is even said to have skied to this engagement himself, a distance of almost 90 kilometres (56 miles). Having beaten the Danes, Vasa was crowned king of Sweden in 1523, founding a dynasty that ruled until 1654 and made Sweden a major European power. The *Vasaloppet*, a famous annual cross-country endurance race, commemorates his long-distance ski-run.

of southern Norway. In 1868, Norheim devised a fluid new way to turn on parallel skis. He also made skis with a waisted and cambered profile that were far better suited to sporting manoeuvres like fast downhill gliding and jumping.

Telemark turns, as they came to be known, involve pressing the heel flat on the 'downhill' (outside) ski, while raising the heel on the 'uphill' (inside) ski with the knee bent. The technique went along with Norheim's new method of fixing the boot to the ski at the heel only, using strong, flexible straps made from birch roots. These 'osier' bindings, as they were called, enabled the skier to twist, jump and turn while skiing downhill. The Telemark turn was largely superseded by the Stem Christie (named after Christiania, the old name for Oslo, where it was invented) in which the skis form a 'V', but the Telemark experienced a revival by enthusiasts from the 1970s onwards.

Norheim emigrated to the USA in 1884 and introduced skiing there. One immediate result was that prospectors used skis to cross tracts of snowy wasteland during the Klondike gold rush of 1896. In 1888, a remarkable feat of endurance captured the public's imagination, when the Norwegian explorer Fridtjof Nansen crossed the Greenland icefield on skis. His account of the expedition became a worldwide bestseller. It was thanks to Nansen that alpine (or downhill) skiing developed at the end of the 19th century. This style of skiing was pioneered by the

military (Norway had used ski troops in combat with Sweden during the Napoleonic Wars of 1807–14). Later, downhill skiing caught on as a leisure activity and transformed some of the mountainous areas of Europe, as skiiers and holidaymakers flocked there.

Rapid change

From around 1930 onwards, skis were reinforced with steel edges to reduce wear and metal guiding grooves were added to the running surface to make turning easier. Meanwhile, safety bindings for alpine skis, which kept the heel firmly fixed to the ski but allowed the toe to release in the event of a crash, made skiing far safer.

Around the same time, people started to apply wax to skis to stop snow sticking to them and so make them run faster. The next major advance came during the huge boom in leisure skiing during the 1950s, when resin and plastic coatings began to be used on a whole range of skis for specialised purposes – cross-country, downhill, slalom, jumping. Some skis dispensed with the wooden core altogether and were made entirely from glass fibre.

Skiers remain in constant search of better performance and bigger thrills, and board sports have mushroomed. The range of modern skis and activities is huge – parabolic 'shaped' skis for off-piste runs, monoskis, snowboards and 'freestyle' skiing. Finally, there is waterskiing, which was first demonstrated by the American Ralph Samuelson in 1922.

Bowls c2000 BC

Hand–eye coordination
An illumination of bowls in a medieval manuscript captures the skill and intense concentration of players involved in the game.

There is some dispute about exactly when and where the game of bowls originated. Some claim it began in Asia Minor in around 9000 BC, but the more prevalent theory is that its birthplace was Egypt. Bowls made of porphyry (a purple crystalline rock), dated to around 5000 BC, were found in the tomb of a young Egyptian nobleman and the game is depicted in wall paintings of around 2000 BC. Later, the ancient Greeks played a version of bowls rather like the modern-day shot-put. The Romans codified the game and introduced it to Gaul, where it became the ancestor of *boules*, or *pétanque*.

Up to the Middle Ages, the bowls were basically round stones, but thereafter they increasingly came to be made of wood.

French tradition
A figurine of a female bowls player from Gaul in Roman times.

The game itself became such a craze that statutes were passed to control and restrict it. In the mid-1300s, Edward III of England and Charles V, 'the Wise', of France both banned bowls because it was distracting their troops from practising archery and swordsmanship. The oldest bowling green still in use is in Southampton, dating from 1299, so the ban did not last too long there. It is not certain whether Francis Drake was really playing bowls on Plymouth Hoe as the Spanish Armada approached on July 21, 1588, but by the 16th century bowls was certainly a popular sport in England for which lawns, precursors of the grass in today's gardens, were carefully prepared and manicured.

We have only a sketchy idea of the rules of the ancient game; the rules governing most variants of the modern game were established in the 19th century. In 1864, for instance, a Glasgow cotton merchant called William Mitchell published the *Manual of Bowls Playing*, from which the current rules of flat-green bowling are derived. In France, the popular game evolved along less formal lines into many regional variants, with the *boules* being thrown rather than rolled. In the 19th century, the *boules* were made of wood, studded with nails; these were replaced in the 20th century by metal ones.

Keys c1500 BC

In parts of Africa and Oceania, you can still find examples of primitive locks. The keys are simple pegs, inserted through a hole in the door, which engage with a bolt on the inside and slide it open or shut. This type of latch existed in China some 4,000 years ago.

The first true keys, dating from about 1500 BC, appeared at roughly the same time in Egypt, India, Japan and Norway. These took the form of long wooden or bronze rods with prongs ('teeth') that pushed loose wooden pins ('tumblers') in the lock out of the hollow recesses ('mortices') of the bolt, so allowing the bolt to slide freely. The particular refinement on the Egyptian form of this type of lock was that keys were made unique by changing the size and number of teeth. The Greeks used a sickle-shaped iron key that lifted a bolt fixed to the inside of the door. The Romans improved upon this by making complex cut-outs in the bit, the component that sets the lock in motion.

Some keys made in the Middle Ages were huge, elaborate works of art. This was the era in which the key became a quintessential symbol of power – the keys of St Peter were believed to unlock the gates of heaven.

From the 18th century, the constant search for greater security saw key technology evolve rapidly, especially with the invention of the pin-tumbler lock by Linus Yale in 1848. It was patented by his son in 1861. Nowadays, high-security locks are increasingly operated by means of swipe cards with magnetic strips or memory chips.

ORIGIN OF THE SKELETON KEY

The story goes that King Henry II of France (r1547–59) built a castle, the Château d'Anet, for his mistress Diana of Poitiers. To ensure that he would always be able to gain access, Henry ordered his locksmith to make a key that would fit every lock in the castle. Thus was born the skeleton key.

Complete kit
A bronze lock and its key (left) from Roman-occupied Palestine in the 1st century AD.

Spoons

c1500 BC

In ancient times, food was scarce and people would have been concerned not to waste the slightest morsel. To make it easier to eat grainy food like cereals, people began using implements such as seashells, hollowed-out stones, or shells from large nuts. Such makeshift utensils were the prototypes of the spoon. The invention of the spoon as such came when these simple tools were refined into longer implements with handles, which enabled food to be picked up more easily.

The first people to use spoons for food are thought to have been the Chinese, in around 1500 BC, although far older examples, probably used for ritual anointing, have been found in Egypt and Mesopotamia. Despite its practicality, the spoon did not become popular

Special commission
Although not widely used until the 15th century BC, spoons were undoubtedly invented earlier. This Sumerian spoon made from a shell (above) dates from c2500 BC.

primarily as a utensil for meals – people continued to use their fingers – but rather for its cachet as a luxury item. Spoons were made from all kinds of durable materials, such as wood, stone and glass. Wealthy Greeks and Romans favoured bronze, silver or gold spoons, often with highly ornate handles.

Decorative spoons reappeared at the end of the Middle Ages, and became steadily more ornate during the Renaissance. Venetian and Tuscan craftsmen turned apostle spoons, with effigies of patron saints incorporated into the handle, into an art form. Little wonder, then, that the common idiom 'born with a silver spoon in his mouth' was coined to describe a man fortunate enough to have a life of ease.

GLASS – c1500 BC

A clear breakthrough

The history of glassmaking is a prime example of how a technology can evolve and become adapted for different purposes down the ages. From its original decorative use in jewellery and scent bottles, it was put to practical service, such as in windows and mirrors. Its latest application is in telecommunications, in the form of fibre-optic cables.

Glass is obtained by a process of fusion – by heating quartz sand (silica) and sodium carbonate (which occurs naturally as natron) in a furnace together at an extremely high temperature of 1300°C. The particular colour of the glass comes from metals and other minerals oxidizing in the process. The first forms of glass were probably a by-product of attempts to reproduce the shiny residue that was sometimes left in the base of metalworkers' crucibles. People discovered that they could use this to coat earthenware pots and vases and give them lustre and colour. These first tentative steps towards glassmaking took place in Mesopotamia and Egypt towards the end of the 4th millennium BC.

Towards transparency

Early glassmakers left blocks of coloured glass to cool, then cut it like obsidian (a natural volcanic glass). Later, they realised they could work glass in its semi-molten state, and began moulding it into pieces of jewellery or small bottles for perfumes and unguents. The technique used was like the lost-wax method of bronze-casting: the artisan plunged a core mould of compacted sand into molten glass and turned it so the glass stuck to it. Once the glass had cooled and hardened, the sand was poured out, leaving a hollow glass vessel in its rough state; the object was finished by smoothing and polishing. The fewer impurities in the raw materials – particularly the sand – the greater the transparency of glass obtained. The manufacture of fully translucent glass was achieved in around 1500 BC. From 300 BC, the glassmakers of Ptolemaic Alexandria excelled in core-formed vessels, which were traded by the Phoenicians far beyond the Middle East.

Around the same time as moulded glass was being perfected, a new technique arose. In the 1st century BC Syrio-Palestinian craftsmen from the area around Sidon and Byblos developed a method of blowing down a metal tube – the blowing iron – into a bubble of semi-molten glass to create a hollow mass. By quickly rotating the blowing iron, and with the help of special tools, it was possible to make beautiful thin-walled glass vessels. The technique of blowing opened up a whole new range of applications for glass.

A multiplicity of forms

The Romans founded the first major glass-making studio in the reign of Emperor Nero (AD 37–68) and

Ancient art
Glass was a favourite material for luxury items in the ancient world. The fish-shaped green glass platter (top) is from 18th Dynasty Egypt (1550–1292 BC), while this painted glass bowl is Roman, from the 2nd or 3rd century AD.

A TALL TALE

If we are to believe the Roman writer Pliny the Elder (AD 23–79), glass was invented as the result of a shipwreck near the Phoenician port of Tyre in the eastern Mediterranean. According to Pliny's *Natural History*, the surviving crew lit a signal fire on a makeshift hearth made of blocks of natron, which they had been transporting as cargo to Egypt where it was widely used in embalming.

Once the fire had gone out, they noticed a sticky, translucent residue left behind – the world's first piece of glass, produced by the fusion of quartz in the sand with sodium carbonate from the natron. An engaging story, but probably not true: the process also requires the presence of lime, which Pliny does not mention, and an open fire is unlikely to reach a high enough temperature to create glass.

spread glassblowing through their empire. From *c*600, glassmakers managed to produce sheet glass by blowing a sphere then allowing gravity to pull it into an elongated 'pod'. While still hot and malleable, the ends of the pod were sliced off and the resulting cylinder cut open lengthways and rolled flat. Alternatively, a sheet of 'crown' glass could be made by spinning the iron so fast while blowing a glass ball that it was flattened into a disc by centrifugal force; this was cut free to leave the 'bullseye' (or 'bullion') pattern seen in many old leaded window panes in northern Europe. By the early Middle Ages magnificent stained-glass windows were being created for Europe's new cathedrals. Venice – in particular the island of Murano – became the glass-making centre of Europe in the 11th century.

From 1675, industrially produced lead crystal – a process using pure quartz sand and lead oxide, patented by the Englishman

Glass beads
During the Iron Age, glass became a precious material used in the manufacture of jewellery, like this necklace from the 5th century BC.

Master craftsmanship
As glassmaking techniques evolved, glass became more transparent and was crafted into ever more elegant shapes. This ornate Roman flask was made in the 3rd century AD.

George Ravenscroft – began to supplant Venetian glass and the handmade crystal of Bohemia. In 1874 a patent was taken out for toughening sheet glass by heating it then cooling it in oil. Reinforced glass was invented in 1893. Laminated safety glass (1909), made from thin layers bonded together, saved the life of French prime minister Georges Clemenceau in 1919, when a bullet failed to penetrate the windscreen of his car. In 1958, British glassmaker Alastair Pilkington invented float glass, which is stretched and floated on a bath of liquid tin before cooling. This process made it possible to manufacture very large sheets of plate glass and also ultra-thin glass for optical instruments.

THE FIRST PLASTIC

The prototype of all plastics was lacquer, invented in China in *c*1300 BC. It came from the sap of the 'varnish tree' (*Rhus vernicifera*). Virtually indestructible and colour-fast, lacquer was used to make a variety of objects, from statues to furniture and tableware. The first modern plastic, celluloid, was created in 1869.

Ancient Egypt – a civilisation of master builders

Without the benefit of mechanical lifting equipment or the wheel, the Egyptians accomplished extraordinary feats of technical genius in erecting their temples and pyramids. Our knowledge of their tools and methods has advanced in recent times, but ancient Egyptian construction sites are still intriguing places providing plenty of material for further investigation.

Temple complex
Sheer cliffs rise behind the vast temple complex at Deir el-Bahri, on the west bank of the Nile opposite Thebes (Luxor), which was built during the reign of Queen Hatshepsut in the 15th century BC (main picture). The pyramids at Giza (above right) are the most famous of ancient Egyptian constructions; the Great Pyramid of Khufu is on the far right.

'Let a permanent monument be built for me, the like of which has not been seen since the days of the Gods.' With this proclamation, Pharaoh Khufu (Cheops), who succeeded his father Snefru in 2589 BC, ordered the building of his mortuary pyramid as his 'eternal abode'. Astronomer-priests, architects, master builders – the cream of Egyptian scholars and engineers – assembled to consult the 'Book of Foundation for Temples', reputedly compiled by Imhotep. Their task was to select the ideal site and determine the direction the building should face. So began the construction of the Great Pyramid of Khufu on the Giza plateau, just south of today's city of Cairo, almost 4,600 years ago.

Hive of activity

First, extensive preparatory work was carried out: the ground was levelled, a canal and dock were excavated, a wide road was built to give access to the site and a ramp was constructed for dragging the stone blocks up to be set in position. The ramps were assembled from bricks made from mud and straw and baked in the sun. Because of their resilience and longevity, these bricks are still a popular building material in the Near East. Intact specimen bricks have been found dating back to Predynastic Egypt, more than 5,000 years ago.

Building Khufu's pyramid was a massive undertaking. Granite blocks for the inner core of the building were brought from Aswan, some 700 kilometres (435 miles) to the south; the external cladding and architectural details were made from a fine-grained white limestone quarried at nearby Tura. Miners at Tura hewed vast subterranean caverns out of the bedrock, reaching up to 50 metres below ground level and linked by galleries. The roof, which in places reached a height of 10 metres, was supported by rock pillars.

The Tura quarry was worked from top to bottom. At the vertical rockface, the limestone lay in horizontal strata separated by thin layers of clay and criss-crossed with fissures that divided it into blocks. The quarrymen would first sound out the fine clay stratification lines, which were hard to make out with the naked eye, by striking the rockface with hammers and listening, or by using their fingertips to detect faint vibrations. To remove a block, they would start by hacking into the rockface with picks made from flint or diorite (a hard form of granite). Then copper chisels were driven deep into the fissures, followed by wooden wedges; the wedges were wetted to expand the

EGYPTIAN WATERWORKS

The ancient Egyptians quickly learned how to use hydraulic engineering to tame the Nile and turn it to their advantage. Because Egypt's climate was wetter in the time of the pharaohs than it is now, the Nile Valley was inundated whenever the river was in full spate. The most pressing task was to built dykes to protect villages from the rising waters.

Dike-building was followed by the construction of a canal network to circumvent the river's many cataracts and make navigation easier. The canal works were a major undertaking. An immense waterway was dug parallel to the Nile; its banks were finished in stone masonry that was regularly maintained. The waterway was known as the Memphis Canal and it linked Middle Egypt to the Mediterranean via the fertile Faiyum Oasis. Built in the First Dynasty, it was still in existence at the time of Napoleon's

Egyptian campaign (1798–1801). The canal was fed by Lake Moeris, northwest of Faiyum, which was replenished by the Nile's annual flood. Remains of a system of sluices and weirs, restored in the 12th Dynasty, have been found at the lake.

Aside from irrigation, the main benefit of the Memphis Canal was that boats could sail up and down it all year without having to battle against the wind and the current. The man-made waterway carried all the materials used to build the royal necropolises. Traces of landing stages can still be seen just below the pyramids.

On the banks of the Nile, the Egyptians established a system of 'nilometers', consisting of wells linked to the Nile by tunnels. The depth of water was read from markings on the nilometer walls, enabling people to monitor the height of the river and so gain warning of floods in time to strengthen dykes and ditches.

wood, levering the blocks away from their bed of clay. The Tura limestone blocks for Khufu's pyramid weighed an average of 2.5 tonnes.

Heavy haulage

The Nile formed the axis for all the major building works that took place in ancient Egypt: all quarries and completed monuments lie in close proximity to the river. Manuscripts discovered at Meidum note 12 dates, scattered throughout year, when materials were delivered to the Giza site, including in the dry season. This contradicted a longstanding theory which maintained that the stone blocks could only have been transported to the pyramids on rafts when the river was in flood. In fact, for the most part the river was not deep enough to be navigated by heavily laden barges. It was Egypt's efficient canal system that allowed vessels to reach the construction sites all year round. They had vessels that were up to the task. From the 3rd millennium BC, they built broad-beamed transport vessels that could carry heavy cargoes. Snefru already had at least two royal barges at his disposal that were 50 metres long.

Once on site, the stone blocks were hauled up the sides of the pyramids on sleds that resembled modern snow sledges. Capable of carrying loads of up to 6 tonnes, the sleds were dragged up shallow-gradient ramps made from mud bricks topped with compacted earth, which was kept wet to allow the sleds to slide smoothly. An attempt by archaeologists to re-create this technique, at Karnak in 1934, demonstrated that a sled carrying a stone block measuring roughly 1 square metre and weighing 2 tonnes could be moved easily by a team of just six people. Experts are still undecided whether the ramps went all the way to the top of the pyramids or stopped some way short, with the last blocks being winched up by a system of ropes and pulleys.

Monolithic stone needles

Over time, ever more massive pieces of stone were quarried and carved into colossal statues and obelisks, then transported using the same methods. Obelisks were symbols of the sun god, Amun-Re, and were erected in pairs outside temples dedicated to him. Usually hewn from single blocks of pink granite, they

Not so hard
*A wall painting from
the 18th Dynasty shows
construction workers
pulling a sled laden with
a huge block of stone.
Research has shown it
was possible to haul
such massive blocks
without too much
difficulty.*

appeared at the start of the 2nd millennium BC. One obelisk, almost 42 metres long and weighing some 1,150 tonnes, was left behind at Aswan – perhaps because cracks began to appear – and has given scholars an insight into how such huge pieces of stone were quarried.

First, using stone hammers, workers marked out the shape of the obelisk by excavating a wide trench in the granite. They then chiselled down, forming the sides to the required depth, before gradually undercutting it via a series of tunnels, which were backfilled as they worked to prevent the piece breaking free and dropping suddenly. Finally, the obelisk was eased out horizontally with the aid of levers and wedges and slid across the quarry floor. The finished obelisk was packed into a wooden casing that was only removed when it had been hauled upright at its final destination. Like all other masonry for Egyptian temples

and monuments, it would be transported to its designated site by barge and sled.

There have been several attempts to re-create the technique for raising a finished obelisk. Archaeologists think it was done by building a flat-topped earth mound, slightly lower than the obelisk's total height, with a steep slope on one side running down to where the obelisk was to be sited. The obelisk was dragged on a sled up a gentle gradient onto the mound, then lowered base-first down the steep incline onto a bed of dry sand. Labourers then dug away the sand until the base of the obelisk came to rest against its pre-positioned plinth. Finally, to manoeuvre the stone upright onto the plinth, a large gang of workers hauled on ropes running through a wooden A-frame to the top of the obelisk. Once up, its own weight and a precisely crafted mounting would keep the monolith firmly in place.

THE MERKHET AND OTHER EGYPTIAN TOOLS

Following both religious and scientific precepts, the priest-astronomers determined the precise siting and orientation of the pyramids. To align the foundations of the structures with the cardinal points of the compass, these ancient scientists relied on observation of the night sky. Astronomers measured the ransit of a star – Sirius, for example – with the aid of an instrument called a *merkhet* and a plumb-line. The *merkhet* was simply a wooden bar with a notch carved in it, which acted as a surveying sight. To use the instrument required two people: one person held the merkhet at arm's length and, looking down the instrument, aligned the notch with a plumb-line held by a second person. This made it possible to determine, from a fixed point, exactly the positions where a circumpolar

A merkhet *(below) and plumb-line (left).*

star rose and set on a level circular horizon. Bisecting the angle made by these two points indicated where true North lay.

The Egyptians had access to other basic tools that are still used by stonemasons today. For example, workmen created perfectly level pieces of ground using spirit levels. The discrepancy in height across the entire breadth of the base of the Great Pyramid of Khufu is only 20mm. Blocks of stone were shaped precisely using a level, a plumb-line and a set square.

The stonemason's trade *Egyptian stonemasons as depicted on an 18th Dynasty fresco (below left). In their work they would have used measuring sticks and plumb-line weights like these (below right).*

CHRONOLOGY

The timeline on the following pages outlines key discoveries and inventions and how they have evolved down the ages.

Technological advances are shown in relation to the major cultural, natural, political and social events and phenomena that marked the prehistory and early history of humankind.

6 million – 1 million years ago		700,000 – 100,000 BC		80,000 BC

EVENTS

- Tertiary Era
- Australopithecines
- *Australopithecus afarensis:* (fossilised skeleton known as 'Lucy' found at Hadar in Ethiopia in 1974)
- *Homo habilis*
- Beginning of the last Ice Age
- End of the Tertiary Era

- Beginning of Quaternary Era
- *Homo erectus*
- *Homo ergaster*
- Beginning of the Lower Palaeolithic (Old Stone Age)
- Early hominids evolve in Africa
- Migration of *Homo erectus* to Europe and Asia

- The Acheulean culture thrives in France

- End of the Acheulean culture
- Beginning of the Middle Palaeolithic

- *Homo sapiens*
- Neanderthal Man
- Beginning of the Mousterian culture

INVENTIONS

- Manufacture of first stone tools – pebblestones chipped away on one face
- Earliest human settlements at Melka Kunture (Ethiopia) and Olduvai Gorge (Tanzania)

- Bifacial flint tools created at Olduvai
- Evidence of fire use in Africa

- Bifacial flint tools of the Acheulean industry first appear in Europe

- Wooden stakes made with stone tools – fossilised remains found in Germany and at Clacton-on-Sea in Essex
- Levallois technique of flint knapping developed
- Stone hatchets used in Africa, Europe and Asia
- Development of the first semi-permanent settlements
- Shaping of flint shards into tools

- First evidence of burial sites

◄ Bifacial stone tool

▲ Flint-knapping

▼ *Homo habilis*

75,000 – 50,000 BC	35,000 BC	30,000 BC	20,000 BC	16,000 BC
• Peopling of Australia	• *Homo sapiens sapiens* • Cro-Magnon Man • Beginning of the Upper Palaeolithic • End of Mousterian culture and beginning of Aurignacian	• Peopling of the Americas	• End of the Aurignacian culture and beginning of Solutrean	• Height of the last Ice Age
• Necklaces made from seashells (South Africa) • Neanderthal burial sites in Kurdish region of Iraq (Shanidàr)	• Fixing of handles to tools becomes more widespread; short, stabbing spears are made of wooden poles with sharpened tips of bone • Mammoth hunters build dwellings out of the bones of their massive prey (Ukraine, Czech Republic, Russia)	• First examples of figurative art, from France (Chauvet caves) and Mexico (Poxte, Jovelte and Canchacan caves) • Clay female figurines made throughout Europe – examples found in France (at Lespugne and Brassempouy), Germany (Willendorf) and Italy (Savignano) • Evidence of first funerary rites in Italy (Grimaldi) and Belarus (Sounguir)	• Stone oil lamps, burning animal fat for fuel, in use in Mesopotamia and Europe • Bone flutes played in southern Europe (example found at Isturiz in the Basque region of France)	• Development of bone sewing needles (found in caves in the Dordogne, France)

◄ Neolithic shell necklace

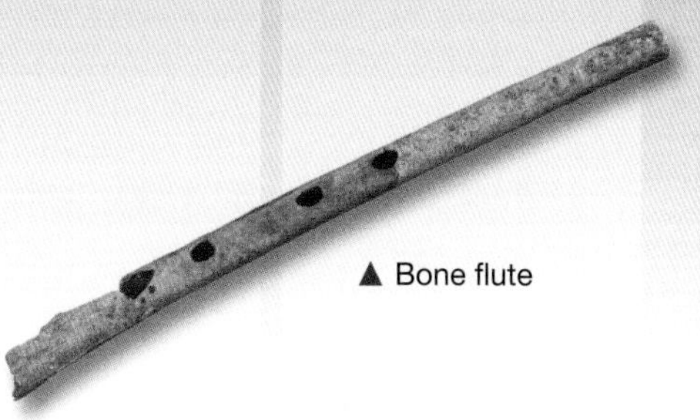

▲ Bone flute

▲ Stone-age hand axe from Abbeville (northern France)

◄ The 'Venus of Willendorf'

Hut made from mammoth bones and hides ▼

147

15,000 BC	13,000 – 12,000 – 11,000 BC			10,000 BC	9000 BC
EVENTS					
• End of the Solutrean culture and beginning of Magdalenian	• Climate begins to warm up			• End of the Paleolithic • End of the Magdalenian culture	• End of the last Ice Age • Beginning of the Neolithic (New Stone Age)
INVENTIONS					
• Cave paintings made at Lascaux in France • Sculpture in bone becomes widespread	• Harpoons used for fishing – found in Dordogne, France • Spear-thrower (atlatl) increases the power and range of a hunter's throw; one example decorated with bird figures and a faun found at Mas d'Azil in the French Pyrenees	• Fire is made by striking flint on iron pyrites to make sparks • Wild cereals (Emmer, einkorn) first cultivated in the Fertile Crescent (Mesopotamia)	• Ceramics decorated with twisted-cord pattern reliefs made in Japan (Jomon) • Sailors in the Mediterranean region use fishing nets • Manufacture of jewellery from polished stone in the Natufian culture of Palestine/Syria • Cave paintings created in Spain (Altamira) • Dogs domesticated in Palestine	• Bow and arrow first depicted in cave art at Arana in southern Spain • Spear tips and arrow heads made from razor-sharp microliths in Europe and the Middle East	• Evidence of early stone masonry at Tell Mureybet in Syria and Ain Mallaha in Palestine • Cattle domesticated in Europe

▲ Bone combs

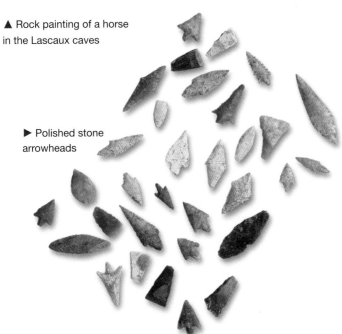

▲ Rock painting of a horse in the Lascaux caves

► Polished stone arrowheads

◄ An Indonesian hunter and his bow

8000 BC	7500 BC	7000 BC	6000 BC	5000 BC	4500 BC
• Further warming of Earth's climate • Beginnings of the transition from nomadic lifestyle to permanent settlements			• Rise of the Indus Valley civilisation • Rise of the El-Obeid civilisation in Mesopotamia	• Beginnings of settled farming civilisation in the Valley of Mexico (Zohapilco)	

8000 BC	7500 BC	7000 BC	6000 BC	5000 BC	4500 BC
• Farming begins with the cultivation of cereals – barley and wheat in the Middle East, sorghum and millet in Africa, maize in the Americas and rice in China • Polished stone axes first made in Palestine • Evidence of basket-making in Spain (at Los Murciélagos) and Egypt • Pine-log boats made in northern Europe – one found in Holland dates from around the same time as a paddle found at Star Carr in Yorkshire • Carved bone combs in use in Scandinavia • Sheep domesticated in Mesopotamia	• Wild vines first appear • Evidence of trepanning, a surgical procedure on the skull (skull found at Ensisheim in Alsace, France) • Goats domesticated in Mesopotamia	• Cultivation of legumes – lentils and peas in Europe, soya beans in China – and of tomatoes and potatoes in the Americas • Use of pottery becomes widespread in Anatolia and the Middle East • Ceramics decorated with reliefs and impress patterns made in the Saharan region of Africa and in Mesopotamia • Bitumen used for waterproofing in Mesopotamia • Pigs domesticated in Mesopotamia • The first towns arise in the Fertile Crescent – Çatal Hüyük in Anatolia, Jericho in Palestine – and shortly after at Lepenski Vir in the Balkans	• Development of the polished stone adze speeds up forest clearance for farming • The stone knife for reaping appears in Europe and the bone-and-flint sickle in Palestine • Construction of stone temples at El-Obeid, Iraq • Manufacture of mud bricks at Jericho • Copper knives, with blades hardened by cold hammering, in use in the Near East • Weaving developed in the Near East • Cotton first processed in India • Beer brewed from various cereals in the Near East	• A sailing boat is depicted for the first time on a Sumerian tomb at Eridu • Madder (a red dye) first used in the Indus Valley	• Megalithic structures (dolmens, menhirs, etc.) erected in Europe • Earliest known fish hook (discovered at Lepenski Vir on the Danube, near the Black Sea) • Birch-sap chewing gum used in Scandinavia • Copper needles appear in Egypt • Papyrus used in Egypt to make ropes, mats and sandals

◄ Sumerian carving of a man with an axe

► Bitumen ceremonial goblet

◄ Neolithic pottery

▼ Artistic representation of a Scandinavian longboat

149

4000 BC   3750 BC   3500 BC   3200 BC

EVENTS

3500 BC
- City of Uruk founded in Mesopotamia
- Peopling of the South Pacific

3200 BC
- The semi-legendary King Narmer (also known as Menes) unites Upper and Lower Egypt and becomes the first pharaoh

INVENTIONS

4000 BC
- First temple-pyramids built in Peru
- Copper mined for the first time in the Near East, at Tal-el-Iblis (Iran)
- The noria (a water-lifting device) is use in the Near East, Africa and Asia
- Harnesses developed for teams of oxen in Mesopotamia
- Horses domesticated in the Ukraine

3750 BC
- Early map drawn on a clay tablet (found in northern Mesopotamia)
- Cosmetics based on red and yellow ochre, kohl and malachite are used by the ancient Egyptians
- The skinned drum is introduced in Upper Egypt, as music becomes part of Egyptian social life

3500 BC
- Proto-hierogylphs appear in Egypt
- First known measurements of time conducted through the alignment of standing stones with the rising and setting sun in Saxony-Anhalt in Germany and at Stonehenge in England
- Arches are built in brick in Mesopotamia and Egypt
- The wooden wheel starts to revolutionise transport in Mesopotamia
- The 'tournette', a basic potter's wheel, is developed in Mesopotamia
- Copper nails are used in Mesopotamia and the first metal saws, also of copper, in Egypt
- Welding develops in Mesopotamia, initially using gold and later copper
- Egyptian women wear perfume
- Silkworms reared in China
- Bee-keeping begins in Egypt

3200 BC
- Development of cuneiform script in Mesopotamia and hieroglyphic writing in Egypt allows records to be kept and inventories made of crops and livestock
- Cylinder-seals used for individual signatures in Mesopotamia
- Viticulture introduced in Egypt and Phoenicia (Lebanon)
- An image of a flute player is made on a plaque in Egypt
- 'Ötzi', a Neolithic hunter, becomes frozen in a glacier in the Ötztal Alps in the Italian Tyrol; he is rediscovered in 1991 complete with clothes, tools and weapons

▶ Sumerian royal chariot

▶ An Egyptian scribe

▲ Cuneiform writing on a stone tablet

◀ Stone circle at Stonehenge

Viticulture in ancient Egypt ▶

3000 BC

- End of the Stone Age
- Beginning of the Bronze Age

- The lost-wax process is used for the first time in bronze-casting in Mesopotamia and the Indus Valley, to make artefacts such as the 'Dancer of Mohenjo-Daro'

- City-states develop from the settlements at Ur, Mari and Ebla in Mesopotamia

- An engraving on a Sumerian cylinder-seal shows the plough was in use in Mesopotamia

- The vitrification process, as a glazing technique for pottery, is invented in Egypt and Mesopotamia; small ornamental objects are manufactured from coloured glass

- Construction of the first water-driven mills

- Soap is manufactured at Sumer by mixing fat with an alkaline lye, marking the beginning of an early chemical industry

- The mirror, wig and brooch become widespread as fashion accessories in the Near East

- The harp is played at Ur in Mesopotamia

- Donkeys are domesticated in the Near East

2700 BC

- Beginning of the Egyptian Old Kingdom
- Birth of the legendary emperors Huangdi in China and Gilgamesh in Mesopotamia.

- Calendar comprising 12 months of 30 days each, starting from the heliacal rising of Sirius, the Dog Star (Sophis), is adopted in Egypt

- Imhotep, an ancient Egyptian architect and doctor (later deified as a god of healing), begins Egypt's age of pyramid-building when he masterminds the construction of the step-pyramid at Saqqara as a burial tomb for Pharaoh Djoser

- Egyptian stonemasons are using plumb-lines and set squares

- Potters around the Mediterranean are using fast, hand-turned potter's wheels

- A set of scales depicted in a fresco at Saqqara shows that such devices were is use in Egypt at this time

- Hemp is used to make rope in China

2600 BC

- Start of acupuncture in China

- Pharaoh Snefru, founder of Egypt's 4th Dynasty and father of Khufu, has large (50-metre) cargo boats built for use on the Nile

2500 BC

- Growth of cities in the Indus Valley
- Growth of the Akkadian Empire in Mesopotamia
- End of the Old Kingdom in Egypt

- Mesopotamians devise a 360-day lunisolar calendar and invent the concept of the hour by dividing the day into 12 periods of equal length

- The peoples of the Indus Valley, in particular at Mohenjo-Daro (modern Pakistan), devise a writing system; it remains undeciphered

- Papyrus is used for writing on in Egypt

- Sewerage and water systems at Mohenjo-Daro are improved by the introduction of clay pipes and the construction of thermal baths

- Early skis in use in Sweden (found in a bog at Hoting)

◀ Votive figurine of Imhotep

◀ Bronze rein-holder

▼ Mesopotamian ziggurat depicted on a cylinder seal

▼ Egyptian merkhet and plumb-line

151

2000 BC	1800 BC	1750 BC	1650 BC	1500 BC

EVENTS

2000 BC	1800 BC	1750 BC	1650 BC	1500 BC
• Beginning of the Egyptian Middle Kingdom • Beginning of the Babylonian Empire • First Minoan palaces built at Knossos on Crete	• Growth of the Hittite Empire • End of the Middle Kingdom in Egypt • Beginning of the Assyrian Empire • Reign of King Hammurabi in Babylon (1793–1750 BC)	• Beginning of China's Shang Dynasty • Demise of Indus Valley civilisation	• Invasion of Egypt by the Hyksos • Beginning of ancient Egypt's New Kingdom	• Start of Egypt's 18th Dynasty • Decline of the Babylonian Empire

INVENTIONS

2000 BC	1800 BC	1750 BC	1650 BC	1500 BC
• The Egyptian Rhind Papyrus, found at Luxor, includes fractions and calculations of areas of land and volumes • Invention of the spoked wheel in Mesopotamia improves transportation of goods and people • Development of a pedal-driven loom in China improves weaving efficiency • Games of bowls illustrated in an Egyptian fresco	• Cuneiform writing on clay tablets becomes the standard way of recording commercial transactions and diplomatic exchanges in Mesopotamia and Egypt • Starting from Ugarit in Mesopotamia, trade connections multiply and flourish between East and West as trade routes criss-cross the Near and Middle East • *The Epic of Gilgamesh* appears, the earliest known work of literary fiction	• Linear A, a Cretan script, is devised; it remains undeciphered	• Chickens are domesticated in India	• The Egyptian Ebers Papyrus describes illnesses and their cures • Chinese doctors treat skin infections with penicillin in the form of a fermented soya poultice • A method of locking a door with a key is devised in Egypt • The first spoons are made in China and Egypt • Glassmakers in the Near East discover how to make transparent glass, giving rise to ever more sophisticated and decorative glass objects

▼ 'Chariot of the Sun', found in Denmark

▲ Fragment of Egyptian papyrus

◄ An Egyptian sundial (left) and gnomon (below)

▲ Egyptian light war chariot (first introduced by the nomadic Hyksos people)

1400 BC	1300 BC	1200 BC	1100 BC	1000 BC	800 BC
• End of the Minoan civilisation on Crete and the beginning of Mycenean dominance	• Decline of the Hittite Empire after defeat by the Egyptians at the Battle of Kadesh	• Rise of the Celtic civilisation • End of the Hittite Empire • End of Egypt's 18th Dynasty	• Decline of the Mycenean civilisation • End of the New Kingdom in Egypt	• The Assyrian Empire centred on Turkey and the Olmec civilisation of Mesoamerica reach their zenith	• Growth of the first Greek city-states • First Olympic Games held (776 BC)

• Invention of the first alphabet, in cuneiform symbols representing sounds, at Ugarit on the coast of what is now Syria

• Bronze artefacts manufactured under the Shang in China

• In Egypt, by royal decree, all doctors became functionaries of the state – in other words, civil servants

• Pharaoh Rameses II orders the construction of a canal between the Mediterranean and Red seas

• The Hittites include 3,500 war chariots in their army to attack the Egyptians

• The Chinese start to use lacquer to decorate furniture, statues and crockery

• The triangular frame harp first appears in Egypt

• Phoenician 'round ships' built

• Start of iron-working in Asia Minor

• A number of collections of pharmaceutical prescriptions are published in the Assyrian Empire

• The Phoenicians sail through the Strait of Gibraltar for the first time

• Kite-flying becomes popular in China

• The 24-letter Greek alphabet is established

• Iron saws used by the Assyrians in Mesopotamia

▲ Roman ship

Glass bowl ▲

▲ Egyptian musicians

▼ The Rosetta Stone

Index

Page numbers in **bold** refer to main entries for a topic; page numbers in *italics* refer to captions.

Picture credits

ABBREVIATIONS : t = top, c = centre, b = bottom, l = left, r = right

B-G = BRIDGEMAN-GIRAUDON

Front cover: main image, tilling and sowing in ancient Egypt, B-G; inset, stone tool, RMN/J.-G. Berizzi/Musée des Antiquités Nationales, Saint-Germain-en-Laye. **Spine**: the Venus of Willendorf, B-G/A. Meyer/Natural History Museum, Vienna. **Back cover**: firelighting equipment from ancient Egypt, RMN/F. Raux/Musée du Louvre, Paris. **Page** 2, left to right, top row: RMN/J.-G. Berizzi/Musée des Antiquités Nationales, Saint-Germain-en-Laye; RMN/Chuzeville/Musée du Louvre, Paris; RMN/H. Lewandowski/Musée du Louvre, Paris; 2nd row: B-G/Museum of Fine Arts, Houston; B-G/Ashmolean Museum, Oxford; RMN/H. Lewandowski/Musée du Louvre, Paris; 3rd row: B-G/Musée du Louvre, Paris; RMN/T. Ollivier/Musée Guimet, Paris; RMN/H. Lewandowski/Musée du Louvre, Paris; bottom row: AKG IMAGES, Paris/Nimatallah/National Museum of Archaeology, Athens; B-G; AKG IMAGES, Paris/Universitätsbibliothek, Heidelberg. **Pages** 4/5: Imagestate/P. Narayan/AGE Fotostock; 6t & b: B-G/Ashmolean Museum, Oxford; 6l: EURELIOS/L. Bret; 6c: RMN/J.-G. Berizzi/Musée des Antiquités Nationales, Saint-Germain-en-Laye; 6/7t: CORBIS/Images.com/E. Dinyer; 6/7c: RMN/J.-L. Hamon/ Musée des Antiquités Nationales, Saint-Germain-en-Laye; 6/7b: RMN/J. Schormans/Musée de la Préhistoire, Les Eyzies; 7c: RMN/J. Schormans/ Musée des Antiquités Nationales, Saint-Germain-en-Laye; 7r: CORBIS/P. Colombel; 8l: EURELIOS/P. Plailly/Fresque de Gilles Tosello; 8c: RMN/J.-L. Hamon/Musée des Antiquités Nationales, Saint-Germain-en-Laye; 8r: AKG IMAGES, Paris/E. Lessing/Museo Egizio, Turin; 8/9b: B-G/Egyptian Museum, Cairo; 9tl: CORBIS/F. Grehan; 9r: B-G/Museum of Ancient Art, Luxor; 10tl: B-G/ Musée de Picardie, Amiens; 10r: RMN/C. Larrieu/ Musée du Louvre, Paris; 10bl: CORBIS/P. Saloutos; 10bc: RMN/R. Lambert/ Musée Guimet, Paris; 11t & tr: B-G/Egyptian Museum, Cairo; 11br: B-G/ Museum of Fine Arts, Houston; 12tl: AKG IMAGES, Paris/E. Lessing; 12tc: RMN/F. Raux/Musée du Louvre, Paris; 12bl: B-G/ Musée du Louvre, Paris; 12r: RMN/F. Raux/Musée du Louvre, Paris; 13l: CORBIS/E. & N. Kowall; 13c: AKG IMAGES, Paris/Nimatallah/ National Museum of Archaeology, Athens; 14tl: RMN/ Chuzeville/Musée du Louvre, Paris; 14bl: B-G; 14r: G. DAGLI-ORTI/Archaeological Museum, Piraeus; 14/15: AKG IMAGES, Paris/ E. Lessing/Mykonos Archaeological Museum; 15tc: RMN/Labat/CFAO/Muée du Quai Branly, Paris; 15r: G. DAGLI-ORTI/National Archaeological Museum, Naples; 15b: G. DAGLI-ORTI/Museo Egizio, Turin; 16t: CORBIS/ Freelance Consulting/D. & J. Heaton; 16bl: RMN/H. Lewandowski/Musée du Louvre, Paris; 16c: RMN/G. Blot/Musée du Louvre, Paris; 16r: CORBIS; 17l: RMN/Musée du Louvre, Paris; 17tr: RMN/Chuzeville/Musée du Louvre, Paris; 17br: B-G/Ancient Art & Archeology Collection, British Museum, London; 18-19: B-G/British Museum, London; 20: RMN/J.-G. Berizzi/Musée des Antiquités Nationales, Saint-Germain-en-Laye; 21b: EURELIOS/L. Bret; 23r: EURELIOS/ C. Pouedras; 22/23t: RMN/J. Schormans/ Musée des Antiquités Nationales, Saint-Germain-en-Laye; 22bl: COSMOS/SPL/John Reader; 23c: COSMOS/ SPL/John Reader; 23r: COSMOS/P. Boulat; 22/23b: RMN/T. Ollivier/Musée Guimet, Paris; 24l: CORBIS/L. Lefkowitz; 24/25: COSMOS/SPL/ K. Kent; 25t: COSMOS/Steinmetz; 25c: RMN/ F. Raux/Musée du Louvre, Paris; 25bl: CORBIS/ P. Johnson; 25br: COSMOS/ANZENERGER/C. Sattlberger; 26t: AKG IMAGES, Paris; 26b: COSMOS/SPL/H. Schneebeli; 27: CORBIS/C. Rainier; 28t: RMN/J. Schormans/Musée de la Préhistoire, Les Eyzies; 28b: AKG IMAGES, Paris/ E. Lessing; 29t: RMN/JL. Hamon/Musée des Antiquités Nationales, Saint-Germain-en-Laye; 29ct, c & b: COSMOS/P. Boulat; 30/31t: CORBIS/ P. Harholdt; 30l: COSMOS/B. & C. Alexander; 31r : RMN/F. Raux/Musée du Louvre, Paris; 31b: CORBIS/P. O'Hara; 32: CORBIS/J. Blair; 33l: Ira Block; 33c: EURELIOS/P. Plailly; 34l: CORBIS/P. Colombel; 34b: RMN/G. Blot/Musée des Antiquités Nationales, Saint-Germain-en-Laye; 34/35: RMN/J. Schormans/Musée des Antiquités Nationales, Saint-Germain-en-Laye; 35r: COSMOS/B. & C. Alexander; 36c: RMN/ C. Larrieu/Musée du Louvre, Paris; 36b: B-G/ W. Neeb/Archaeological Museum of the South Tyrol, Bolzano; 36/37th: RMN/H. Lewandowski/ Musée du Louvre, Paris; 37b: B-G/British Museum, London; 38l: RMN/R. Lambert/Musée Guimet, Paris; 38/39b: CORBIS/Archivo Iconografico SA/Egyptian Musuem, Cairo; 39tl: B-G/Archives Charmet/Bibliothèque de l'Arsenal, Paris; 39b: CORBIS SYGMA/M. Yassubovich; 39r: Martin Archery, Walla Walla, WA 99362; 40t: RMN/ Lebee/Musée du Louvre, Paris; 40b: AKG IMAGES, Paris/W. Forman; 41tl: RMN/JL. Hamon/Musée des Antiquités Nationales, Saint-Germain-en-Laye; 41tr: CORBIS/J. Dickman; 41c: CORBIS/Asia Art & Archeology Inc; 42l: EURELIOS/P. Plailly/Fresque de Gilles Tosello; 42/43t: RMN/G. Blot/Musée Ladevèze, Le Mas-d'Azil; 43tr: EURELIOS/P. Plailly; 43c: RMN/J. Schormans/Musée des Antiquités Nationales, Saint-Germain-en-Laye; 43cr: RMN/ J.-G. Berizzi/Musée des Antiquités Nationales, Saint-Germain-en-Laye; 43b: EURELIOS/P. Plailly/ Fresque de Gilles Tosello; 44t: CORBIS/G.H.H. Huey; 44b: CORBIS/D. Mason; 45t: B-G/Ashmolean Museum, Oxford; 45l: RMN/Chuzeville/Musée du Louvre, Paris; 45br: B-G/Musée des Tapisseries, Angers; 46t: B-G/Vitlycke Museum, Tanum; 48lc: COSMOS/P. Maître; 46b: COSMOS/B. & C. Alexander; 46/47: CORBIS/W. Kaehler; 48t: B-G; 48b: B-G/Egyptian Museum, Cairo; 50t: B-G/ Museo della Cvilta Romana, Rome; 50b: B-G/ British Library, London; 50/51c: CORBIS/ N. Wheeler; 51t: B-G; 51r: CORBIS SYGMA/ P. Giraud; 52/53: CORBIS/L. Nelson; 52: RMN/H. Lewandowski/Musée du Louvre, Paris; 52/53b: AKG IMAGES, Paris/E. Lessing/Museo Egizio, Turin; 53t: B-G/Ashmolean Museum, Oxford; 53r: RMN/J. Schormans/Musée des Antiquités Nationales, Saint-Germain-en-Laye; 54t: B-G/Topham Picture-point/British Museum, London; 54b: CORBIS/ C. & A. Purcell; 55t: CORBIS/K. Su; 55cl: CORBIS/ P. Almasy; 55br: RMN/Chuzeville/Musée du Louvre, Paris; 56t: B-G/Davies, Mrs Nina de Garis/ Ashmolean Museum, Oxford; 56b : B-G/National Museum, Aleppo, Syria; 57t: RMN/ H. Lewandowski/Musée du Louvre, Paris; 57b: CORBIS/D. Conger; 58t: RMN/G. Blot/Musée des Antiquités Nationales, Saint-Germain-en-Laye; 58bl: RMN/R. Schirimpff/Museo de Oro, Bogota; 58br: B-G/Ashmolean Museum, Oxford; 59: B-G; 60/61: CORBIS/H. Stadler; 60c: RMN/J.-G. Berizzi/ Musée des Antiquités Nationales, Saint-Germain-en-Laye; 61tl: B-G/A. Meyer/Natural History Museum, Vienna; 61r: RMN/J.-L. Hamon/Musée des Antiquités Nationales, Saint-Germain-en-Laye; 61b: B-G/Musée Régional du Kosovo, Pristina; 62t: B-G/Museum of Fine Arts, Houston; 62b: RMN/E. Laser/Musée du Louvre, Paris; 65: B-G; 64l: RMN/J.-G. Berizzi/Musée des Antiquités Nationales, Saint-Germain-en-Laye; 64r: RMN/R. Lambert/Musée Guimet, Paris; 65t: B-G/Musée de Picardie, Amiens; 65cl: CORBIS/Gallo Images/R. de la Harpe; 65b: CORBIS/K. Fleming; 66t: B-G/H. Sceebeli/ Musées Royaux d'Art et d'Histoire, Brussels; 66b: RMN/H. Lewandowski/Musée du Louvre, Paris; 67t: B-G/Birmingham Museums & Art Gallery; 67b: RMN/P. Pleyet/Musée Guimet, Paris; 68/69t: AKG IMAGES, Paris/E. Lessing/British Museum, London; 68c: CORBIS/P. Saloutos; 68b: AKG IMAGES, Paris/W. Forman/Museo Nacional de Antopologia, Mexico; 69b: COSMOS/ R. Frerck; 70tl: AKG IMAGES, Paris/Camera-Photo/Museo Civico Correr, Venice; 70tr: RMN/H. Bréjat/Musée Guimet, Paris; 70b: COSMOS/ G. Monnot; 71t: CORBIS/B. Krist; 71l: B-G/Museum of Fine Arts, Houston; 71r: CORBIS/K. Ward; 72t: COSMOS/P. Maître; 72l: B-G; 73t: RMN/ J.-G. Berizzi/Musée des Antiquités Nationales, Saint-Germain-en-Laye; 73l: B-G/Museo Nazionale, Rome; 73br: RMN/H. Lewandowski/ Musée du Louvre, Paris; 74t: RMN/J.-G. Berizzi/ Musée des Antiquités Nationales, Saint-Germain-en-Laye; 74b: B-G/Ashmolean Museum, Oxford; 75t: B-G/The Stapleton Collection; 75b: CORBIS/ E. & N. Kowall; 76/77t: AKG IMAGES, Paris/ Nationalmuseet, Copenhagen; 76c: B-G/National Museum, Damascus; 76b: RMN/H. Lewandowski/ Musée du Louvre, Paris; 77br: RMN/C. Larrieu/ Musée du Louvre, Paris; 78t: B-G/Egyptian Museum, Cairo; 78cl: AKG IMAGES, Paris/ E. Lessing/Federseemuseum, Bad Buchau; 78cr: CORBIS/Michael Maslan Historic Photographs; 78b: CORBIS/Bettmann; 79t: CORBIS/ M. Garanger; 79b: COSMOS/SPL/K. Guldbransen; 80t: AKG IMAGES, Paris/Modern Times, a film by Charlie Chaplin, 1936 © Roy Export Company Establishment; 80cr: CORBIS/Alan Schein Photography; 80b: CORBIS/Duomo; 81t: B-G/ Abbey of Montecassino, Italy; 81c: RMN/H. Lewandowski/Musée du Louvre, Paris; 81b: G. DAGLI-ORTI/Museum of San Marco, Florence/detail from Le retable de la Sainte Trinité, Fra Angelico, 1435; 82t: RMN/T. Ollivier/Musée Guimet, Paris; 82bc: B-G/Ashmolean Museum, Oxford; 82/83: B-G/Egyptian Museum, Cairo; 83br: B-G/Musée du Louvre, Paris; 84l: B-G; 84c: B-G/P. Willi/Musée des Beaux-Arts, Grenoble; 84/85b: B-G/Museo Archeologico, Florence; 85c: AKG IMAGES, Paris/Museum für Ostasiatische Kunst, Cologne/Calligraphie de Yang Lizhoui, 2001; 85r: CORBIS/M. Everton; 86tl: B-G/National Museum, Damascus; 86tr: B-G/British Museum, London; 86bc: G. DAGLI-ORTI/Musée Archéologique, Héraklion; 86br: Bookmaker; 87t: RMN/F. Raux/Musée du Louvre, Paris; 87b: RMN/T. Ollivier/Musée Guimet, Paris; 88t: B-G/Museo Egizio, Turin; 88l: B-G/Ashmolean Museum, Oxford; 88/89b: B-G/Musée du Grand Rabbinat, Jérusalem; 89c: AKG IMAGES, Paris/Visioars/ Bibliothèque Nationale de France, Paris; 89b: CORBIS/P. Johnson; 90l: B-G; 90/91b: G. DAGLI-ORTI/Archaeological Museum, Venice; 91c: G. DAGLI-ORTI/Bibliothèque d'Ajuda, Lisbon; 91r: RMN/F. Raux/Musée du Louvre, Paris; 92tr: RMN/G. Blot/Musée des Antiquités Nationales, Saint-Germain-en-Laye; 92l: AKG IMAGES, Paris/ E. Lessing/Kunsthistorisches Museum, Antikensammlung, Vienna; 93t: CORBIS/C. & J. Lenars; 93l: CORBIS/D. Muench; 93br: G. DAGLI-ORTI/Egyptian Museum, Cairo; 94t: RMN/J.-G. Berizzi/Musée du Quai Branly, Paris; 94bl: RMN/C. Jean/Musée Guimet, Paris; 94br: RMN/Musée des Antiquités Nationales, Saint-Germain-en-Laye; 95t: AKG IMAGES, Paris/Nimatallah/National Museum of Archaeology, Athens; 95b: COSMOS/ P. Maître; 96t: AKG IMAGES, Paris/E. Lessing/ Pergamon Museum, Berlin; 94l: CORBIS/ N. Wheeler; 97t: RMN/Département des Antiquités Orientales, Musée du Louvre, Paris; 97b: SRD; 98t: ALTITUDE/Y. Arthus-Bertrand; 98b: COSMOS/ ASPECT Picture Library/J. A. Langley; 99t: COSMOS/P. Maître; 99c: C. Huyghens; 99b: MNHM/Photothèque; 100/101t: CORBIS/ N. Wheeler; 100r: CORBIS/N. Wheeler; 100b: CORBIS/E. & N. Kowall; 101r: EURELIOS/B. Bireau; 102l: RMN/J. Galland/Musée du Louvre, Paris; 102br: COSMOS/AURORA/P. Essick; 103t B-G; 103b: RMN/H. Lewandowski/Musée du Louvre, Paris; 104: COSMOS/M. Henley; 105t: B-G/Musée du Louvre, Paris; 104/105b: CORBIS/K. Houghton; 106t: RMN/H. Lewandowski/Musée du Louvre, Paris; 106b: CORBIS/C. Lisle; 107t: RMN/ Chuzeville/Musée du Louvre, Paris; 107b: B-G/ Charles Edwin Wilbour Fund/Brooklyn Museum of Art, New York; 108tl : B-G/Musée du Louvre, Paris; 108tr: RMN/J. Galland/Musée du Louvre, Paris; 108b: RMN/H. Lewandowski/Musée du Louvre, Paris; 109: B-G/National Museum, Tehran; 110t: B-G/Ashmolean Museum, Oxford; 110l: G. DAGLI-ORTI/Musée Déon, Châlons-sur-Saône; 110b : B-G/Ashmolean Museum, Oxford; 111b: G. DAGLI-ORTI/Villa Giulia, Rome; 112l: G. DAGLI-ORTI/Archaeological Museum, Piraeus; 112b: Fondation de Coubertin; 112/1134: G. DAGLI-ORTI/National Museum, Athens; 113tr: B-G/P. Freeman; 114t: CORBIS/P. Colombel 114/115b: B-G/British Museum, London; 115tl: CORBIS/N. Wheeler; 115tr : CORBIS/P. Colombel; 115br: AKG IMAGES, Paris/E. Lessing/National Museum, Beijing; 116t: RMN/J. Galland/Musée du Louvre, Paris; 116l: AKG IMAGES, Paris/ E. Lessing/Musée du Louvre, Paris; 116br: G. DAGLI-ORTI/Museo Egizio, Turin; 117t: RMN/F. Raux-S. Hubert/Musée du Louvre, Paris; 117b: RMN/G. Blot/Musée des Antiquités Nationales, Saint-Germain-en-Laye; 118tr: RMN/M. Beck-Coppola/Musée des Antiquités Nationales, Saint-Germain-en-Laye; 118bl: CORBIS/J. Hawkes; 119t: B-G/Musée du Louvre, Paris; 119b: G. DAGLI-ORTI/Topkapi Museum Library, Istanbul; 120 & 121l: B-G; 121r: B-G/K. Welsh; 122t: G. DAGLI-ORTI/Museum of Roman Civilization, Rome; 122cl: G. DAGLI-ORTI/Musée du Louvre, Paris; 122b: RMN/J.-G. Berizzi/Musée du Louvre, Paris; 123t: B-G/Ashmolean Museum, Oxford; 123r: B-G/Bibliothèque Nationale de France, Paris; 124/125: AKG IMAGES, Paris/E. Lessing; 124l: RMN/H. Lewandowski/Musée du Louvre, Paris; 125r: G. DAGLI-ORTI/Egyptian Museum, Cairo; 126l: CORBIS; 126b: CORBIS/J. Feingersh; 127t: B-G/Archives Charmet/ Bibliothèque/Nationale de France, Paris; 127b: RMN/T. Ollivier/ Musée Guimet, Paris; 128tl: G. DAGLI-ORTI/Musée du Louvre, Paris; 128tr: RMN/Musée du Louvre, Paris; 128b: G. DAGLI-ORTI/Musée du Louvre, Paris; 129: CORBIS/K. Su; 130t: B-G; 130b: RMN/Chuzeville/Musée du Louvre, Paris; 131t: B-G/Roger-Viollet/Museum of Roman Civilization, Rome; 131c : B-G/British Museum, London; 131b: RMN/Chuzeville/Musée du Louvre, Paris; 132t: RMN/H. Lewandowski/ Musée du Louvre, Paris; 132b: G. DAGLI-ORTI/Archaeological Museum, Piraeus; 133t: B-G/Archives Charmet/ Bibliothèque Nationale de France, Paris; 133b: G. DAGLI-ORTI/Musée Cernushi, Paris; 134/135: CORBIS/B. Winsett; 134l: AKG IMAGES, Paris; 135t: AKG IMAGES, Paris; 135b: VANDYSTADT/ Zoom; 136t: RMN/Bulloz/Musée Historique et Archéologique, Orléans; 136bl: AKG IMAGES, Paris/Universitätsbibliothek, Heidelberg; 137t: RMN/Musée du Louvre, Paris; 137b: RMN/G. Blot/Musée du Louvre, Paris; 138t: B-G/Ashmolean Museum, Oxford; 138b & 139r: RMN/H. Lewandowski/Musée du Louvre, Paris; 139l: RMN/G. Blot/Musée des Antiquités Nationales, Saint-Germain-en-Laye; 140/141: AKG IMAGES, Paris/E. Lessing; 141t: CORBIS/Freelance Consulting/D. & J. Heaton; 142t: CORBIS/R. Wood; 142b: B-G/Ancient Art & Archeology Collection, British Museum, London; 142/143: AKG IMAGES, Paris/E. Lessing; 143c: G. DAGLI-ORTI/Musée du Louvre, Paris; 143bl & blc: AKG IMAGES, Paris/ E. Lessing; 143brc & br: RMN/F. Raux/Musée du Louvre, Paris; 144/145: B-G; 146t & b: COSMOS/ SPL/John Reader; 146c: EURELIOS/L. Bret; 147tl: RMN/G. Blot/Musée des Antiquités Nationales, Saint-Germain-en-Laye; 147tc: RMN/J. Schormans/Musée des Antiquités Nationales, Saint-Germain-en-Laye; 147tr: RMN/Musée des Antiquités Nationales, Saint-Germain-en-Laye; 147bl: B-G/A. Meyer/ Naturhistorisches Museum, Vienna; 147br: MNHM/ Photothèque; 148tl: B-G; 148tr: B-G/Ashmolean Museum, Oxford; 148bl: RMN/G. Blot/Musée des Antiquités Nationales, Saint-Germain-en-Laye; 148br: COSMOS/B. & C. Alexander; 149l: RMN/ Lebee/Musée du Louvre, Paris; 149tc: RMN/ J.-G. Berizzi/Musée des Antiquités Nationales, Saint-Germain-en-Laye; 149r: RMN/H. Lewandowski/Musée du Louvre, Paris; 149br: B-G/Vitlycke Museum, Tanum, Sweden; 150tl: RMN/H. Lewandowski/Musée du Louvre, Paris; 150tc: B-G/Ashmolean Museum, Oxford; 150tr: B-G/Egyptian Museum, Cairo; 150bl: CORBIS/ J. Hawkes; 150br: B-G; 151l: B-G/Musée du Louvre, Paris; 151tr: RMN/H. Lewandowski/Musée du Louvre, Paris; 151bc: AKG IMAGES, Paris/ E. Lessing/Pergamon Museum, Berlin; 151br: G. DAGLI-ORTI/Musée du Louvre, Paris; 152tl: AKG IMAGES, Paris/Nationalmuseet, Copenhagen; 152tr: B-G/British Museum, London; 152bl: G. DAGLI-ORTI/Musée du Louvre, Paris; 152br: B-G/Egyptian Museum, Cairo; 153tl: RMN/H. Lewandowski/Musée du Louvre, Paris; 153tr: B-G/Museo della Civita Romana, Rome; 153bl: B-G; 153br: B-G/British Museum, London.

Parchment background reproduced on pages 28, 49, 57, 71, 72-3, 81, 87, 94-5, 106-7 and 136-7 supplied by Stockphoto.com/Mike Bentley.

Illustration of the Ziggurat of Ur on pages 15 and 97 is by Jean-Benoît Héron.

The maps on pages 49 and 111 were translated from French by Alison Ewington.

THE ADVENTURE OF DISCOVERIES AND INVENTIONS
The First Inventions – Prehistory to 1200BC
is published by The Reader's Digest Association Limited,
11 Westferry Circus, Canary Wharf, London E14 4HE

Copyright © 2009 The Reader's Digest Association Limited

The book was translated and adapted from *Les Première Inventions*, part
of a series entitled L'ÉPOPÉE DES DÉCOUVERTES ET DES INVENTIONS,
created in France by BOOKMAKER and first published by Sélection du
Reader's Digest, Paris, in 2005.

Translated from French by Peter Lewis

Series editor Christine Noble
Art editor Julie Bennett
Designer Martin Bennett
Consultant Ruth Binney
Proofreader Ron Pankhurst
Indexer Marie Lorimer

Colour origination Colour Systems Ltd, London
Printed and bound in China

READER'S DIGEST GENERAL BOOKS
Editorial director Julian Browne
Art director Anne-Marie Bulat
Managing editor Nina Hathway
Head of book development Sarah Bloxham
Picture resource manager Christine Hinze
Pre-press account manager Dean Russell
Product production manager Claudette Bramble
Production controller Sandra Fuller

Copyright © 2009 The Reader's Digest Association Far East Limited
Philippines Copyright © 2009 The Reader's Digest Association Far East Limited
Copyright © 2009 The Reader's Digest (Australia) Pty Limited
Copyright © 2009 The Reader's Digest India Pvt Limited
Copyright © 2009 The Reader's Digest Asia Pvt Limited

We are committed to both the quality of our products and the service we provide to our
customers. We value your comments, so please feel free to contact us on 08705 113366
or via our website at **www.readersdigest.co.uk**

If you have any comments or suggestions about the content of our books, you can
email us at **gbeditorial@readersdigest.co.uk**

CONCEPT CODE: FR0104/IC/S
BOOK CODE: 642-001 UP0000-1
ISBN: 978-0-276-44513-2
ORACLE CODE: 356400001H.00.24